The Fieldfare

HAMLYN SPECIES GUIDES

THE FIELDFARE

David Norman

HAMLYN

COVER ILLUSTRATION *Fieldfares often feed on apples in winter, particularly in hard weather.*

First published in 1994 by Hamlyn Limited,
an imprint of Reed Consumer Books Ltd
Michelin House, 81 Fulham Road, London SW3 6RB
and Auckland, Melbourne, Singapore and Toronto

ISBN 0 600 57961 1

A CIP catalogue record for this book is available from the British Library

Page design by Jessica Caws
Maps by Louise Griffiths
Printed in Hong Kong

CONTENTS

Fieldfares usually feed on berries for a minute or two and then rest for about 20 minutes.

Series Editor's Foreword

Of all the commoner thrushes that we see in Europe, the Fieldfare must surely be the most attractive: its varied plumage of soft grey, chestnut and black, with white underwing-coverts and bold black spotting on a buffy breast, make it much more colourful than the rest.

In Britain, we see it mostly as a winter visitor, at times in large flocks, feeding in fields and along the hedgerows on the invertebrates and the berries that sustain it through the cold months of the year. When spells of harsh weather with freezing conditions render its normal habitats no longer tenable as places to find sufficient food, huge numbers often invade our suburbs and even town centres, and it then becomes, for a few days, a delightful addition to urban wildlife, its loud 'chack-chack' call soon becoming familiar to people who would normally be quite unaware that this most interesting of thrushes existed at all. Then the birds disappear, as suddenly as they came, and will probably not be seen again in those built-up areas for many winters to come.

Although many Fieldfares die when caught out by severe winter weather, this species is basically a survivor. Exceptionally harsh conditions in Europe in the mid-1930s forced many to flee instinctively westwards, out over the North Atlantic, where death would surely follow. Yet, incredibly, some reached Greenland, managed somehow to survive the extreme and inhospitable winter climate there, and even successfully colonized that island as a new breeder.

Only a handful of Fieldfares breed in Britain, but this is a common nesting bird in Scandinavia and much of Continental Europe, including the high-lying southern parts of the Alps eastwards. It is a surprising fact that many Fieldfares nest in loose colonies, a habit unique among thrushes. This species also lays the largest clutch of all the thrushes. It has a particularly unpleasant, but highly effective, method of defending its nest against predators: it flies up and defecates on them! When a number of birds from a colony do this together, the result is easily imaginable – and can leave an aerial intruder, such as a Buzzard, incapable of flight.

Most birdwatchers have a particular 'feeling' for the Fieldfare, and will find many further intriguing facts about this unusual thrush in David Norman's fascinating text. Relatively little has been published on this species in English, and we owe the author a debt of gratitude for making so many aspects of its life available to a wide audience.

David A Christie

Acknowledgements

There are several people who have helped me in studying Fieldfares. Digby Milwright discussed the results of his researches into ringing recoveries of the species. David Okill and Peter Harris provided information on Fieldfares in Shetland and Portugal respectively, and Dr Mário A. Silva sent me details of ringing recoveries in Portugal. Dr C.G. Wiklund, Dr T. Slagsvold, Dr O. Arheimer and Dr W. Lübcke kindly sent me reprints of their published work and made useful comments. The British Trust for Ornithology sent a copy of the relevant part of their report on hunting of migratory species. Dr Linda Birch, Librarian of the Alexander Library, Edward Grey Institute of Field Ornithology, University of Oxford, greatly helped with searching of the literature. My knowledge of the species could not have developed without the cooperation of Mr and Mrs A. Tustin, who allowed me free access to Daresbury Fruit Farm, Cheshire. Fellow members of Merseyside Ringing Group helped me to catch Fieldfares there.

1

A SUCCESSFUL AND GREGARIOUS BIRD

In 1678, John Ray, arguably the first British ornithologist, wrote of the Fieldfare:
'These birds fly in flocks together with Stares [Starlings] and Redwings. They shift places according to the seasons of the year. About the beginning of autumn come over incredible flights of them into England, which stay with us all winter, and in the spring fly all back again, not one bird remaining; insomuch that (as far as ever I could hear) there has never been seen young Fieldfare or Redwing, or so much as a nest of those birds with us in England. Whither they betake themselves, or where they breed is not to us perfectly known: it is by some reported that they breed in Bohemia; others tell us with much confidence, in Sweden. They have a hoarse chattering note, not much unlike a Magpie; by reason the sides of the fissure in the palate are rough, as we conjecture.'

This is a remarkably accurate summary of the status and behaviour of the Fieldfare, although, of course, modern study and communications have filled in the gaps and confirmed some of Ray's suspicions. A handful of pairs, and rather more Redwings, are now known to nest annually in Britain, but they breed commonly throughout most of Scandinavia and much of the eastern half of Europe.

Fieldfares often flock together with Redwings and Starlings for feeding, although when they fly the species often split up and behave differently.

Unusually for a thrush, the Fieldfare nests in colonies and indulges in furious communal defence by flying at predators and defecating over them with spectacular accuracy. Merlins and other species often nest in the middle of Fieldfare colonies and benefit from their aggression in keeping away owls and larger raptors.

Fieldfares quit the breeding areas to move south and west for the winter, at which time millions, almost exclusively from Scandinavia, visit Britain and Ireland. The wintering flocks are wary, usually staying in the middle of fields and well away from man, but freezing weather can force thousands to gather in hawthorn hedges and orchards, apples in particular giving them vital sustenance in hard times.

Description

The Fieldfare is a large, tough, harsh-voiced, skewbald thrush, different in character and habits from all other British birds. It is a little smaller than the Mistle Thrush, but the two might be confused at a distance, although in flight the Fieldfare never covers such distances on closed wings as does the larger bird. It flies rather like a bee-eater, with strong but easy strokes interrupted by pauses just enough to break the rhythm without introducing the bounding up-and-down pitch of the Mistle Thrush. It is a fairly fast flier, and will rise to heights of 100 m or more for all but the shortest movements. It is more conspicuously gregarious than any other similar-sized bird, and any large flock of thrushes can usually be presumed to be Fieldfares, although one really needs to see some detail or to hear their distinctive voice to be sure.

Although slightly smaller than Mistle Thrushes, Fieldfares are similar in build and proportions, but their peculiar bearing and variegated colouring give a very distinct impression. On the ground the Fieldfare is alert and rather upright, often holding its neck somewhat withdrawn into the shoulders and with the head and bill pointing upwards at an angle of 20 or 30 degrees to the horizontal. The soft french-grey of the head and nape and the rump contrasts with the ruddy-chestnut back and the black wings and tail, while underneath the thick bold spotting of the upper breast is set off by the rich buff ground colour and again contrasts with the white lower breast and belly and, in flight, the underwing. Max Nicholson wrote that the effect is as if 'a conventional brown-backed spotted breasted thrush had undergone some strange mutation half-way towards a brilliant plumage pattern, and there remained, neither one thing nor the other'.

Fieldfares are about 25.5 cm (10 ") in length, with a wingspan of around 40 cm (16 "). Structurally, their wings are typical of all thrushes. The third primary, numbered from the outside, is the longest, with the fourth about 1–2 mm shorter, the second and fifth primaries 5–10 mm shorter and the sixth primary 20–25 mm shorter than the wing point. The third to fifth primaries are emarginated on their outer webs. This shape is close to the classic shape for long-distance migrants. The tail is almost square, with the outermost feathers about 5 mm shorter than the rest.

They are a little shorter than Mistle Thrushes, but proportionately longer-tailed. Their plumage is more boldly variegated and richly coloured than that of any other West Palearctic thrush, with a blue-grey head, chestnut back, grey rump and almost black tail. The underparts are white, heavily speckled black on the breast, and the white underwing is obvious in flight. No other species has the combination of grey rump, black tail and white underwing, and the commonest call, 'chack-a-chack', is unlike any other bird's. Their legs are dark brown, those of the male appearing almost black, and the soles of the feet are yellowish. The iris is dark brown and the bill is orange-yellow with a dark tip, the male's bill changing in breeding plumage to a clear yellow. Some individuals show a fairly clear white supercilium, often interrupted on each side of the eye, that contrasts markedly with the black lore and the black eye-stripe and moustachial stripe.

Juveniles show the characteristic thrush-like speckling on the upperparts, and have a creamy supercilium like a Redwing's. Young birds also show obvious white shaft-streaks on the crown, nape and upperparts. After the post-juvenile moult it is fairly straightforward to determine the age of all Fieldfares at close quarters (either in the hand or with a good view in the field): first-year birds retain some juvenile greater coverts, usually smaller than the moulted feathers, with lighter-coloured fringes, and have narrower, more pointed tail feathers; the primary flight feathers

Fieldfares are occasionally found with aberrant plumage, such as this white-headed adult female that I caught in Cheshire.

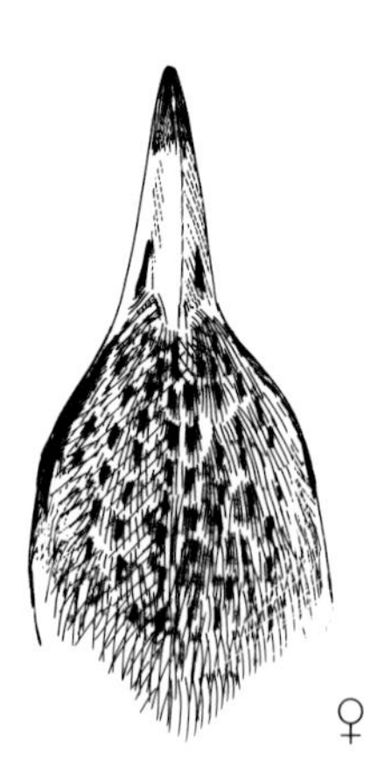

Male and female Fieldfares usually differ in the markings on the crown feathers and bill, especially in the breeding season, but are seldom as obvious as this pair.

of first-years are usually more worn and more pointed than those of adults (see the illustration on page 71).

Birdwatchers can often determine the sex of Fieldfares on the basis of their plumage, although it is not always straightforward as some books imply. For over twenty years the Swedish ornithologist Lars Svensson has researched birds in the hand and as museum specimens to produce 'the ringers' bible', the *Identification Guide to European Passerines*. Svensson notes that the pattern of the crown feathers is the best criterion for sexing, but some birds appear ambiguous. Males tend to have rufous-brown feathers on the back, with blackish centres. Their tail feathers are blackish to black, with the proximal parts of the central tail feathers (nearest to the body) dark grey, if not black. The female's back feathers tend to be rufous-brown to duller earth-brown, with their centres sometimes a little darker but not blackish. Female tail feathers are a dull dark brownish-olive.

The main difficulty in sexing is that older birds have more intense colours than first years. Adults have darker mantle feathers and darker tails, although only males have black centres to the mantle or tail feathers. Also, adults have more extensive black in the head-feathers than first-years. Thus, an adult female appears to have a blacker-looking head than a first-year female, and she may often look blacker than a first-year male. These characters change during the winter as the grey edging preferentially wears off. For the birds I have ringed in England in winter, the colour of mantle feathers and tail seems to be a more reliable sexing characteristic than the pattern on the head feathers. There are also differences in the markings of the breast and flanks, with males tending to be darker slate-grey and females lighter in colour, but these are not reliable sexing characteristics on their own. In breeding pairs it is usually possible to tell the male from the female by the contrast between them.

Occasionally, Fieldfares show aberrant plumage, particularly white feathers. One depicted by Lübcke and Furrer (1985) has three white primaries on one wing, three white secondaries symmetrically on each wing, and other odd white plumage including one tertial, one tail feather, some alula feathers and most of its head. A white-headed female that I caught in Cheshire is shown in the photograph on page 11. An almost black Fieldfare was noted in Middlesex in 1866.

Fieldfares and their relatives

The Fieldfare is a member of the *Turdus* genus of thrushes, along with some of the commonest and best-known species in northern Europe, including the Blackbird and Song Thrush. The family Turdidae comprises about 300 species worldwide, and includes two subfamilies, the Enicurinae (forktails) and the Turdinae (chats and thrushes). There are about 33 genera of chat, and the thrushes are placed in about 15 genera. The latter include, in the Western Palearctic, *Monticola* (Rock Thrush and Blue Rock Thrush), *Zoothera* (White's Thrush and Siberian Thrush), and the visitors from the Nearctic, *Hylocichla* (Wood Thrush) and *Catharus* (Hermit Thrush, Swainson's Thrush, Gray-cheeked Thrush and Veery); and finally the true thrushes *Turdus*, which make up some 65 species including, as well as our subject the Fieldfare, its close relatives Tickell's Thrush, Ring Ouzel, Blackbird, Eye-browed Thrush, Dusky Thrush, Black-throated Thrush, Song Thrush, Redwing, Mistle Thrush and American Robin.

The taxonomic classification into family and genus has traditionally been made on the basis of the physical structure of the birds together with behavioural traits and other ecological factors. Nowadays, increasing emphasis is placed on work in the laboratory on DNA (deoxyribonucleic acid), the self-replicating molecule carrying the basic genetic code. Similarities between species can be determined by mixing their DNA and analysing the extent to which they contain complementary sequences of the nucleotides within DNA.

This revolutionary approach has revealed some surprising relationships and led to proposals for a different basis to taxonomy. Fortunately for the purposes of this book there is no major change to the classification of the thrushes. In this new scheme the family Turdidae includes two subfamilies, the true thrushes Turdinae and the Muscicapinae, the latter containing the two tribes Muscicapini (Old World flycatchers), and Erithacini (the chats).

What makes a thrush? In essence, it is a medium-sized song bird whose young generally has a spotted first plumage. As with almost all European

Figure 1.1 *Thrush measurements.*

Species	Body length	Wing (male)	Wing (female)	Tail	Tarsus	Bill
Mistle Thrush	265	143–164	143–162	100–117	30–35	22–25
Song Thrush	230	111–123	110–123	77–90	31–35	20–23
Blackbird	265	116–135	118–128	95–110	32–34	23–27
Ring Ouzel	270	134–150	132–147	101–110	33–36	23–25
Redwing	208	111–133	110–128	76–95	29–31	19–22
Fieldfare	255	140–159	135–156	100–110	31–34	23–25

All dimensions are in mm.

The data are from Cramp (1988), with the addition of my wing lengths for Fieldfares.

passerines, they have ten primary feathers (remiges) on each wing and twelve tail feathers (rectrices). The structural characteristics shared by all thrushes include well-developed and anisodactylic feet, (three toes facing forwards and one to the back), with tarsi that are booted (in an undivided piece, rather than with overlapping scales) and acutiplantar (making a pronounced angle between leg and foot). They have rictal bristles above the slender bill. Their tongues are blade-shaped, with a reedy tip.

In habits, thrushes are largely terrestrial. Most of the genus nest mainly in trees but feed mainly on the ground. They typically feed on both invertebrates and fruits. Many of the larger thrushes can uncover hidden food by sweeping with the bill and simultaneously scratching with one foot, a feat of coordination that is confined to a few bird families. In the breeding season, they are generally monogamous and lay blotched eggs with a bluish or greenish ground colour. Normally, the female alone builds the nest, which is often strengthened with mud, and she incubates and broods the young, but both adults feed their chicks.

All the above are general characteristics applying to the thrush family as a whole. Of course, there are differences between the species, but these are smaller than the differences between the thrush family and birds in other families. Six of the thrushes are common in northern Europe: Mistle Thrush, Song Thrush, Blackbird, Ring Ouzel, Redwing and Fieldfare. The Mistle Thrush is the largest, both in overall length and in wing length, with Fieldfares and Blackbirds the next biggest in body size, but Fieldfares are longer-winged.

The Redwing is the smallest, being appreciably smaller than the Song Thrush in length from bill tip to tail, although their wing lengths are similar. Blackbird males and females differ distinctly in plumage, with the sex differences in Ring Ouzels similarly discernible, females being much browner than males. With Fieldfares it is possible to tell their sex by careful examination of plumage colours, while there are no perceptible differences in the other three species.

It is a fundamental fact in ecology that no two species can occupy exactly the same niche. Much of the separation comes about from structural differences, particularly in body size, and strength and size of feet and bill, which are linked to differences in food and feeding behaviour. In the thrush family, the ecological isolation is achieved by a combination of these factors. Eric Simms suggests that bill size is one of the most important, as with Darwin's finches on the Galapagos Islands, and Simms' measurements of the product of average bill length and depth for all six British thrush species show the Fieldfare to be the fourth largest. The Song Thrush and Redwing are much smaller than the other four. The foot structures of the thrushes follow the same trends as their bill sizes.

From a British viewpoint, Fieldfares are mainly thought of along with Redwings, since both are best known as winter visitors in large numbers, often forming mixed flocks. Fieldfares are probably the most characteristic hard-weather birds, yet they may arrive as early as August or September and stay until May, or even June or July. One May Day near Selborne, the

---

RIGHT *Members of the thrush family that are common in northern Europe (from top): Blackbird, Ring Ouzel, Redwing, Song Thrush, Mistle Thrush and Fieldfare.*

village made famous by Gilbert White's detailed eighteenth century natural history writings, Max Nicholson saw a flock of sixty or seventy Fieldfares fly over a hedge containing fully fledged young Mistle Thrushes.

Fieldfares belong naturally to the fringes between open and wooded country. Although they like open ground, large exposed areas far from cover do not appeal to them. They need big fields or grassy wastes, dry or damp, with rough pasture and arable land preferred, but with easy access to tall trees. They generally avoid large dense blocks of woodland, but also occur regularly in sparser woodland where there are berries such as those of Rowan, Holly, Yew, Dog Rose and Hawthorn. They were recorded in three-quarters of all woodlands surveyed for the BTO's Habitats Register.

While the weather remains mild the higher ground is occupied by Fieldfare flocks of varying size, often consorting with Redwings, Mistle Thrushes and Starlings. Cold weather soon moves these flocks down into more enclosed areas where berries are more available. If hard weather continues for more than a few days, numbers dwindle rapidly as the birds move on, but they return as soon as a thaw sets in.

Fieldfares in history and literature

The Fieldfare has long been a part of the European avifauna. It must have been in the bird communities of the birch forests that arrived in Britain in the pre-Boreal phase, following the retreat of the tundra in the last Ice Age. Fossils have been found from the Late Ice Age (Upper Pleistocene), between 11,000 and 150,000 years ago. The earliest European civilizations were certainly well aware of it. The Romans regarded Fieldfares as delicate eating, keeping thousands of them in aviaries where they were fattened on a paste of bruised figs and flour. They, and Redwings, were almost deprived of light, fed well and then sold for 3 *denarii* each. Martial, the first century Roman poet, wrote to a friend that he would gladly send him a birthday present if he could supply him with fattened Fieldfares.

It is not surprising that a bird as obvious as the Fieldfare should be mentioned by authors of old. Fieldfares appear in the literature in the ninth century, but it was probably Chaucer (1340-1400) in his *Parlement of Foules* who first encapsulated the way most Britons think of them as 'Above all the birds of winter, the frosty feldefares'.

The nineteenth century English poets produced some memorable phrases, clearly based on acute observations. Matthew Arnold must have watched them feeding: 'Hollies with scarlet berries gemm'd, the fellfare's food'. Wordsworth wrote of 'the fieldfare's pensive flock', although he rather romantically thought that 'love of fellowship' rather than 'dependence on mutual aid' was the reason for their flocking. John Clare, in his 'March' poem from the *Shepherd's Calendar* (1827), manages within four lines of poetry to refer accurately to their feeding and flocking habits, winter movements and spring migration:

'... flocking fieldfares, speckled like the thrush,
picking the red haw from the sweeping bush
that come and go on winter's chilling wing
and seem to share no sympathy with spring.'

Names

Fieldfares are striking birds, and have long excited the attention of country folk. The species has been given names in different countries appropriate to various of its habits. Its English name comes from the Anglo-Saxon *feldefare* or *feldeware*, pronounced as four syllables and meaning field traveller. Various corruptions of this are found in its local name in many parts of Britain, such as feltyfare (Midlands), fildifare (Shropshire), feltiflier (Scotland), felfer (Lancashire), felfaw (North Riding of Yorkshire), velverd (Wiltshire), felt or cock felt (widespread in England), and falk (found locally on the Northamptonshire/Buckinghamshire border).

In some other countries it also is named after its habitat, as in the Swedish *Björktrast* and the old German *Birkendrossel* (birch thrush), and the Danish name *Fjeldtrost* (field thrush). After it improbably colonized Greenland, the locals named it *orpingmiutarssuaq*, meaning the big bird of the willow shrub. The Spanish know it, the biggest of their thrushes, as *zorzal real*, the royal thrush. The fact that the Fieldfare becomes more evident to man during hard weather brings the local English name of 'snow bird' and the colloquial Swedish 'snow-magpie'.

The Fieldfare is named after its diet by the Germans (*Wacholderdrossel* – Juniper thrush) and the Russians (*Ryabinnik* or *Drosd-Ryabinnik* – Mountain Ash thrush), although the Dutch *Kramsvogel* (small eating bird) probably refers to its reputation, known to the Romans over 2000 years ago, as being good for humans to eat! Its recent habit of resorting to orchards in hard weather would probably earn it the name of apple thrush.

Its colours have led to other names, including the Norwegian *Gråtrost* (grey thrush, also encountered in Scotland), the old German *Blauziemer* (blue back) and *Blaudrossel* (blue thrush), and such local names in various parts of Britain and Ireland as blue tail (in the Midlands and the West Riding of Yorkshire), blue bird (Devon, West Cornwall), blue back (Lancashire, Cheshire, Shropshire), and blue felt or blue pigeon (Ireland).

The Fieldfare's voice has earned it yet more names, such as jack bird (locally in England), *Jhackert* (Luxembourg), *claque* (in Normandy), *Sjagger* (Denmark), *Schacker* (Germany) and *tordella gazzina* (chattering magpie-thrush) colloquially in Italy, the official Italian name being *tordella cesena*. In some parts of Britain it is known for its harsh cry before rain (although it is not clear whether the bird has been confused with the Mistle Thrush), and is called storm bird (Norfolk), storm cock (Shropshire, Scotland), screech bird or screech thrush (Stirling), and shred cock (Shropshire).

The species' scientific name originates, as do so many, from Linnaeus in 1758, *Turdus* being the thrush genus, and *pilaris* of uncertain origin, but probably derived from the Latin *pilus*, a hair, and perhaps referring to the ancient habit of catching Fieldfares in fine hair traps.

Races

The Fieldfare breeds half-way around the world and might be expected to have evolved into distinctly recognizable races. The differences between birds from different areas are, however, slight and are masked by the

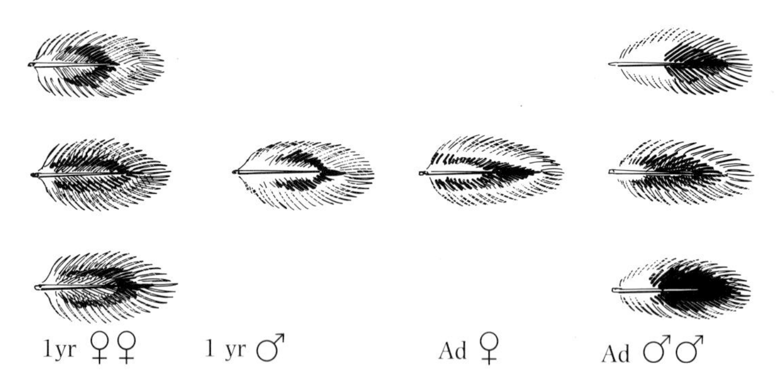

The range of individual variation in the sex-difference of the shape of dark coloration on crown feathers, showing the normal patterns, but also how a first-year male can look 'female'.

individual variations, and no distinct races are recognized. The clinal variations seem to follow the 'rules' deduced and named by various workers. These include Bergmann's rule, that the body size tends to be larger in cooler parts of the range and smaller in warmer areas; and Allen's rule, that the extremities, particularly the bill and legs, tend to be shorter in the cooler regions and longer in the warmer parts of the range. The adaptive basis for both of these rules is thought to be the reduction in heat loss in cold climates, as it is for Gloger's rule, that races in warm and humid climates are apt to be more heavily pigmented than those in cool and dry areas. Fieldfares from different regions, however, do not obviously follow this trend in colour. From west to east, reddishness decreases, with overall fading of the upperpart colours, and wing length increases. From north to south, there is a decrease in the blackness of the tips of the breast and throat feathers, with rusty hues predominating in southern birds.

Thus, birds of the southern population from central Europe and western Siberia, east to the Yenesei, tend to be slightly smaller than those from northern Europe, and to have a more red-brown colour to the mantle and scapulars, with more rusty-brown and less black in the spotting on the underparts; this population is sometimes separated as *T. p. subpilaris*. Populations east of the Yenesei are, on average, larger and paler, with paler grey on the head and rump, paler rufous on the mantle and scapulars and less deep buff on the underparts, sometimes separated as *T. p. tertius*.

Male Fieldfares appear to have longer wings than females in every population that has been measured. In my study of Fieldfares, presumably of Fennoscandian breeding stock, ringed while feeding in Cheshire orchards in winter, I found significant age- and sex-dependent differences in the measurements of mean wing lengths, with values of 151.9 mm (adult males), 147.5 mm (adult females), 150.0 mm (first-year males) and 146.1 mm (first-year females). The wing measurements of these Cheshire birds were much larger than those published elsewhere, probably because my study birds were from the northerly end of a clinal variation, with larger wings, as expected from Bergmann's rule.

Adult Fieldfares are bigger than first-year birds of each sex, with the age-related differences for males greater than for females. The mean wing lengths for adult males are longer than for adult females by 4.4 and 5.0 mm in my study and that of Lidauer and Dieberger (1983) respectively, while for first-year birds the differences are 3.9 and 3.6 mm. Many other studies have found adults to be longer-winged than first-year birds in a wide variety of species. The suggested explanation is that shorter wings are more manoeuvrable, while longer ones are better for fast flight, and there may be an evolutionary pressure for young birds to manoeuvre well.

It is not so simple to give typical weights for Fieldfares. Birds' weights change markedly through the day, with accumulation of fat as a reserve to be converted into energy during periods when they cannot feed, such as through long cold winter nights. Thus, daily weight changes of a few per cent are normal, and greater variations are experienced at times. Prior to migration, birds may add substantial deposits of lipids to fuel their extended flights over the sea. Fieldfares' weights are usually in the range 100 – 120 g, depending on the size of the individual bird. Hard weather, however, can cause extreme changes, as discussed further in Chapter 8, with some emaciated Fieldfares almost halving in weight before they become too weak to fly. At all times of year, the weight to some extent reflects the individual's general condition, with better-fed birds more likely to breed and overwinter successfully, and to be higher in the social-dominance order.

A Fieldfare in a classical pose with its head tilted slightly to one side, perhaps listening for worms.

A gregarious bird

Many Fieldfares nest in colonies, most of them gather together for migration, and in winter it is quite unusual to see one on its own. They are clearly among the most sociable of passerines. They often mix with other species, particularly Redwings and Starlings, for feeding, although if the flock is disturbed, perhaps by a predator, the species usually quickly split up and behave differently. Even within flocks, most birds maintain a certain distance from each other. Although this distance has not been measured for Fieldfares, it is typically several body lengths for most species, about 0.5 m, and a bird infringing this 'personal space' will be threatened.

One other activity that is undertaken communally is the overnight roosting. At any time outside the breeding season, from June or July onwards, large roosts gather in pines or other coniferous woodland, particularly in young plantations, in deciduous woods with a dense understorey of laurel or rhododendron, or in tall hedgerows or willow or Hawthorn scrub. In central Europe they also use alder plantations and osier beds, and they shared an Austrian roost, in reeds at the edge of the Danube, with Blackbirds and Yellowhammers. It is not unusual for Fieldfares to roost on the ground on ploughlands, stubble or marshes, or in long grass or heather. Gilbert White thought it odd that a bird that spends much of its daylight hours feeding in hedges and nesting in high trees 'always appears with us to roost on the ground'. He noted that they came in just before dark and settled in flocks among the heath in the forest. Fieldfares were also frequently taken by catchers of Skylarks, dragging nets over stubble fields at night, whilst the bat-fowlers, who took many Redwings from hedgerow roosts, never caught Fieldfares.

Their roosts can be difficult to trace, as the birds often travel long distances and seem to sneak away from their feeding sites during the afternoon without any great demonstration. In fact, I never found the normal roost site of the flocks of Fieldfares that I spent so much time studying. In long spells of cold weather, I found some birds in the Cheshire orchard on moonlit nights: they appeared to be on the ground and may have been roosting, but it is possible that they were feeding on apples during the night. These could have been birds which were in poor condition, too light to fly off to roost, although it would be risky for them to sleep in the orchard owing to the presence of foxes. I have been ringing for ten years at a roost of thrushes in rhododendrons under mixed mature trees of oak, birch, Yew and pine, where the main species present is Blackbird, normally about 500 birds but in some winters perhaps up to 1000, augmented at times by Redwings, sometimes in very large numbers, maybe 5000. The only time that Fieldfares have been present was during January 1986, in very cold weather, when about 50 of them joined the other thrushes for a week or two, another indication that extreme weather can modify their roosting behaviour.

Most Fieldfare roosts in Britain are of 300–1000 birds, but there were an exceptional 25,000 at Brandon in Warwickshire in late March 1977. Fieldfares are said to roost in their thousands in the Netherlands, and a

Fieldfares usually drop almost vertically into their roost site.

roost of 200,000 formed in January 1975 in the département of Nord in France, sharing the site with Blackbirds.

Their behaviour at a roost usually follows a predictable pattern. At one site in France, birds gathered in flocks of variable size to fly to the roost. A few might arrive shortly before dusk and assemble in the highest treetops, then suddenly dive, along with the rest of the flock, into the roost, sometimes silently but sometimes with a sharp 'chack' call. When the weather was bad, towards mid-winter, all the birds arrived together. In a winter roost of several hundred Fieldfares and Redwings that I watched in a young spruce plantation in rural Cheshire, the Fieldfares arrived late, 15–30 minutes after sunset, and flew in high before dropping straight into the middle of the wood. Birds roosting in an area of willow scrub in April, however, arrived at least an hour before sunset, and the time of arrival may just indicate how well fed they are, with mid-winter birds needing to use every possible minute of daylight to feed. Although they typically drop in from a height, birds often work their way to the shrub layer, sometimes less than 1 m above the ground, to find a sleeping place. Fieldfares usually leave their roosts in the morning well before it is light, with a rattle-call from one bird perhaps waking the flock, which responds with a general clamouring.

Why do Fieldfares roost together? Several theories have been advanced on the value and function of communal roosting. The coordinated pre-roost flights and the simultaneous entry to the roost probably serve to confuse potential predators and thus minimize the risk of death for any individual bird. An interesting hypothesis is that a roost acts as an information centre, especially for where to find good feeding sites. Communal roosts are normally composed of those species whose food is patchily distributed, locally superabundant and ephemeral, so that there is no advantage to be gained from trying to defend such a food source, or to try to keep secret the knowledge of its whereabouts. Conversely, birds not knowing of a good site would gain by learning from others. The suggestion is that birds that had fed well the previous day would leave the roost in a direct way, heading for yesterday's site, and birds that were seeking a better feeding area would wait until they see others purposefully heading off and would then join them. The food distribution of Fieldfares, however, does not fit the above description, except in hard weather when the ground is frozen and fruits are in short supply.

Roost-sites may simply be the best places to keep warm overnight. If it is a 15-minute flight each way to the roost, say 8 km, that takes a Fieldfare roughly an extra 30 kJ of energy, and removes half-an-hour from the possible feeding time. The energetics of a Fieldfare's day are discussed in Chapter 3, but flying off to a distant roost is worthwhile in energy terms only if the roost offers the bird a local temperature increase over the ambient of as much as 12°C. Clearly, this is normally impossible, although on very windy nights the reduction in 'wind chill' afforded by a good sheltered roost site may approach this figure: measurements at a Blackbird roost in scrub in north London found an average wind speed within the roost only one-quarter of that outside. Some species, such as Wrens and Long-tailed Tits, huddle together for warmth at night, but most others, including thrushes, keep their usual distance from each other, and there is no direct benefit for Fieldfares of keeping each other warm.

2

DISTRIBUTION AND POPULATION

Fieldfares have expanded their range, particularly since about 1950, and there are recent breeding records from every country in Europe except Portugal and Eire. They remain mostly northern birds, however, and they breed at higher latitudes, and also at higher altitudes, than most passerines. Originally a taiga-dweller of mid and west Siberia, the Fieldfare has now spread to the transition zone between shrub- and wooded-tundra and wooded 'islands' in the steppes. In Scandinavia and the east it is mainly a summer visitor, whereas in central Europe the birds are generally present all the year round, although local breeders may move out in winter to be replaced by immigrants from breeding areas farther north. In western Europe the relatively small numbers breeding are dwarfed by the millions that move in for the winter from Scandinavia and central Europe, Fennoscandian birds mixing freely in winter with birds of central European stock. The species has a wide breeding range in west Siberia, from the wooded edge of the steppes in the south into the tundra in the north, these west Siberian birds wintering mainly in the region of the Black and Caspian Seas, including the eastern side of the Caspian, where they are joined by Fieldfares of central and east Siberian breeding stock.

Describing the historical expansion of the species' breeding range in Europe can give problems owing to the many changes in political geography that have occurred, mainly during the twentieth century. I have used the name and boundaries of each country as they now are, but often linked them to the physical geography with the name of a river or a mountain range, or the name of a former political region (such as Bohemia) when this does not cause confusion. Readers who spend a little time with this chapter and a good atlas will find themselves transported in their imagination to some magical faraway places.

Breeding range

The boundary of its breeding area, shown in Figure 2.1, extends across Europe from north Norway to the Murmansk coast, across the Kanin peninsula, the mouth of the Pechora, the south Ob region, at least to 70°N on the Yenesei, and maybe as far as 73°N in the Taimyr peninsula, north of the mid-Siberian mountains and thence eastwards to just beyond the Lena river. The boundary then turns south to Ust'Maya on the Aldan river at 60°30'N, 135°E, their easternmost regular breeding site, thence south to the course of the Amur in east Siberia and across towards the Yablonovyy mountains east of Lake Baikal. From there, the limit of its

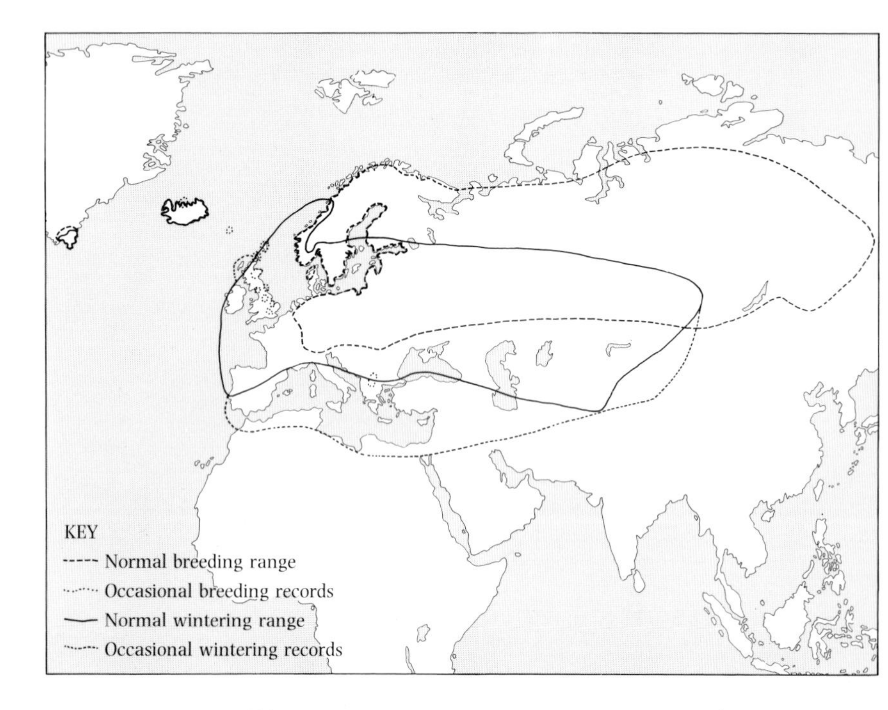

Figure 2.1 *Fieldfare breeding and wintering areas.*

range skirts the northern edge of Mongolia, through the Sayan and Altai mountains to Semipalatinsk and Karaganda in Kazakhstan. It roughly follows the 52°N parallel through Ural'sk, Saratov, Voronezh, and well south of Kiev in the Ukraine to Czechoslovakia and Austria, generally avoiding the lower-lying ground but with southward extensions in the Carpathian mountains in Romania and to Ljubljana in Slovenia. Thence the normal breeding boundary follows the southern Alps in Italy and France west to approximately 2°E, then northwards to the Belgian coast.

Regular breeding records outside this range come from Britain and Iceland, with occasional records from the Faroes, Greenland, the Spanish Pyrenees, Macedonia, Greece, and possibly the north-west Sinkiang province, China.

For the past 100 years or more the species has been slowly extending its breeding range westwards in Europe south of the Baltic. Formerly occurring from Siberia through Poland into East Germany, it spread into West Germany during 1850 – 1900 and still continues to expand its range there. Switzerland was reached in 1923 and the French Jura in 1953. The increase in breeding range then accelerated, and in 1960 Fieldfares first nested in Denmark. Breeding was suspected in Italy in 1963 and proved in 1968. They first bred in Romania in 1966 and in Yugoslavia in 1975. The first Fieidlfares breeding in Britain and Belgium were recorded in 1967, and juveniles were seen in Luxembourg in August 1969 and July 1970 before nesting was first proven in May 1971. After a handful of records in the first half of this century, regular breeding in the Netherlands began in 1972.

This expansion is illustrated in Figure 2.2. In addition to colonizing new countries, Fieldfares are still spreading to fill in areas within their normal range from which they had formerly been absent. For instance, in Poland they have recently reached Biebrza in the north-east, and in Germany they are still spreading, from the south-east, in Westphalia.

During the last 25 years, amateur birdwatchers in most countries of Europe have conducted nationwide censuses aimed at producing comprehensive atlases of breeding birds. Several atlases of winter distribution of birds have also been published, and one year-round national atlas, for the Netherlands. The descriptions of breeding and wintering distribution given in this chapter are based on the published atlases from the countries cited, supplemented by other, more recent, information when available.

The largest colonies, many of them hundreds of pairs strong, are found in western Norway, where the familiar *Gråtrost* nests down to the shoreline. In the eastern districts of Norway it has more of an alpine form, comparatively scarce near the coast and in the valleys but common

Figure 2.2 *The spread of the Fieldfare's breeding range across Europe during the twentieth century.*

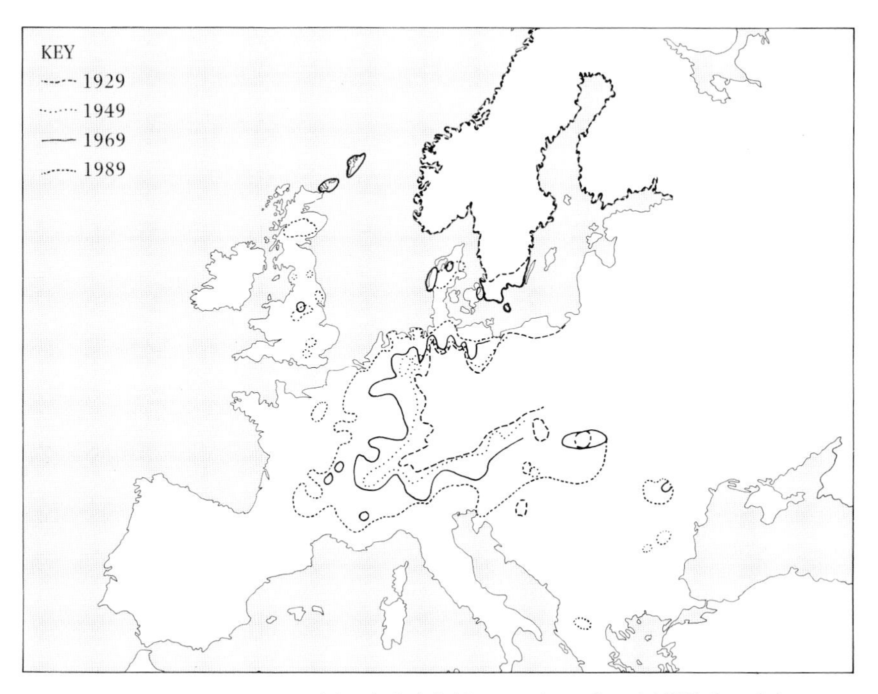

The status in Eastern Europe, particularly in the first half of the century, is not well-recorded. Within the marked boundaries, breeding is not always continuous or widespread.

enough on and above the birch-clad slopes of the fjelds, where it is often found breeding at over 1200 m above sea level. Fieldfares are also plentiful in the woods within the Arctic Circle; some of the colonies here rival those of the west coast in size. Further to the north, as the birch trees diminish in stature, finally being replaced by scrub, the birds become less numerous.

Even on the open country, however, a few pairs raise their young every summer, and nests have been found even in so bleak a situation as the island of Vardö off the east coast of Finnmark, while fieldwork in the late 1980s for the breeding atlas for Finnmark found that they regularly breed on the islands of Ingöy and Hjelmsöy, at over 71°N. In Sweden, the Fieldfare breeds from the southern tip to the frontier with Arctic Norway, its great strongholds being in the north; it is are distinctly scarcer in southern Sweden, south of about 57°N, but has slowly spread into the Skåne region since the 1960s.

Fieldwork for the breeding atlas of Finland was carried out in 1974–9, and Fieldfares were found in 77 per cent of the 10 x 10 km square mapping units, with breeding proven in 76 per cent of these. They were almost ubiquitous in the south, as far north as 65°N, thinning out considerably beyond the Arctic Circle, but even there they were present in about half of the squares and proven to breed in over one quarter.

Although they are one of the commonest birds in the other Scandinavian countries, it was not until 1960 that Fieldfares first bred in Denmark, when newly fledged young were found in Zeeland and in west Jutland. The first nest was found in 1965, in west Jutland, with another in north-west Jutland in 1966 and a colony there the following year that had grown to 40 pairs by 1969. This strong expansion in the late 1960s mirrors that in southern Sweden at the same time. In the years up to 1987, the species' range in Denmark was still expanding from the north-west to south-east, and it had reached the island of Bornholm.

In middle Europe, the longest-settled area of breeding Fieldfares comprises a wide part of eastern Germany, although several intriguing phases of range expansion and contraction have been observed over the course of the last 100–150 years. By 1880, the species had become almost as common as the Blackbird in some areas, but by 1900 it entered a marked regressive phase. After some years of absence, it was then found again in the Thüringer range by the late 1920s, but in the 1930s it apparently vanished again as a breeder in east Thüringer Wald.

The 1950s, however, saw the start of the recolonization of the Gera district, south-west of Leipzig, where Fieldfares quickly spread and in 1967 were said to be the commonest of the thrush family. Nowadays the species is almost ubiquitous in eastern Germany, except for the districts adjoining the Baltic coast.

Fieldfares have colonized central and western Germany since 1830. Their spread through Germany has been painstakingly researched, town by town and village by village, and is spelled out in the *Handbuch der Vögel Mitteleuropas*. Some significant landmarks include breeding in the vicinity of Stuttgart in 1840, Kassel in 1894, Munich in 1900, and north-east of Hannover in 1927. The breeding-bird atlas for the former Federal Republic of Germany, carried out in the 1970s, showed the Fieldfare to be widely

A Fieldfare fluffed up against the cold. The square tail feathers and uniform coverts are characteristic of an adult.

distributed and proved breeding in most of the census units except for a major part of the north-west of the country, roughly west of a line from Lübeck through Hamburg, Bremen and Osnabrück to Aachen. Its expansion continued during the atlas period: of the 120 units (50 x 50 km square) surveyed in 1975 it was present in 102, while by 1980 it was found in 110.

Although present in most areas, Fieldfares were much more difficult to find breeding west of the Rhine, having colonized Rheinland only since the mid-1960s, where they originally inhabited altitudes mainly above 150 m. They are clearly still expanding there, and now spreading to the lower plains. In Saarland they first bred in 1973, with the first nest in the suburbs of Saarbrucken in 1979. In the 1979–83 breeding atlas for the German Land of Bavaria, Fieldfares were found in 98 per cent of the 10 x 10 km squares, with breeding proven in 86 per cent. After a major expansion, starting in the last decades of the nineteenth century, the species' position stabilized in the 1970s, and it is now almost ubiquitous.

Fieldfares first colonized Switzerland, from the north-east, in 1923, and within half a century, by the time of the 1972–76 Swiss breeding atlas, they were breeding throughout 85 per cent of the country. They are scarce and irregular in the canton of Geneva, which they first reached in 1965, and absent from much of the highest-lying land in Valais and the Bernese Alps, although even there they struggle way above the tree-line and place their nests on alpine chalets, with a number of records above 2000 m, to

A pair of Fieldfares at their nest on an Alpine chalet above the tree-line in Switzerland.

as high as 2400 m. The main areas they had failed to colonize were in Ticino, where breeding was recorded first in 1975, but only sporadically since, mainly in the north part of the canton.

The first breeding in France was recorded in 1953, near the Swiss border, with records in adjacent areas coming in 1955, but the species spread only slowly, with no other départements being colonized until 1961, when it reached the Vosges and Haute-Savoie. It continued to push westwards from the mid-1960s, and especially from 1970 onwards, when its progress accelerated. During the French breeding-atlas project, for which the fieldwork was carried out in 1970–75, breeding was proven in most areas in the easternmost nine départements adjoining Germany and Switzerland. After this, a south-westward expansion took off in the mid-1970s into the Dauphine sub-Alps and Fieldfares reached parts of the Massif Central from 1979, in which year an isolated pair bred near Versailles, just west of Paris. During the 1980s, the spread to the west and south-west apparently still continued.

In the Netherlands, isolated breeding occurred in 1903, 1905 and 1909. Nests found in 1935 and 1936 in the north-east of the country were thought to be overspill from the German population, and another pair bred in 1955. In the early 1970s, summer records became more regular, with breeding proven from 1972 onwards. The start of the Dutch increase in Fieldfares coincided with the Netherlands breeding-bird atlas, which covered the years 1973–77. In those five years, Fieldfares were confirmed breeding in 22 of the recording blocks (each of about 25 km^2 in area), nine of them in the south Limburg stronghold, but with the other thirteen scattered widely through the eastern half of the country; probable breeding was recorded in a further 24 blocks, and possible breeding in as many as 103 areas. In total, Fieldfares were recorded in the breeding season in about 9 per cent of the country.

Belgium organized its atlas survey in the same five years, and pioneered attempts to assess the numbers of breeding birds in addition to recording their breeding status. The results give an amazing indication of the success of the species. After first breeding in Belgium in 1967, Fieldfares had, by the end of the atlas period only ten years later, bred in almost a quarter of the country's 457 census blocks (each of about 65 km^2 in area) and the population had reached at least 3700 pairs. The population was assessed in the range 125–625 pairs in as many as fourteen of the census blocks, with 25 logging 26–125 pairs, 39 containing 6–25 pairs and 34 holding 1–5 pairs. Starting from a small colony in the region of the Ardennes mountain range in eastern Belgium, Fieldfares have spread rapidly to occupy much of the region east of the river Meuse, with the westward expansion still apparently in progress.

Although the first nest in Luxembourg was found only in 1971, Fieldfares quickly extended their breeding range and density, and had colonized the whole of the Grand Duchy by the end of the latter's atlas survey period, which lasted from 1976 to 1980. The country was mapped in 5 x 5 km units, and Fieldfares were present in the breeding season in 88 per cent of the 129 squares, with most of the empty squares being those around the edges of the country that were not surveyed as well as the rest. Breeding was proven in 92 squares.

Fieldfares are now fairly numerous breeders in lowland areas in the east of Poland, and have recently increased considerably in the south-west, after being scarce and local there. Until the beginning of the nineteenth century, they bred only in the north-east of the country. In the 1820s numerous broods were found in Pomerania and Silesia, and this situation continued until about 1920, when strong decreases occurred in those regions. Elsewhere in Poland, Fieldfares expanded in 1950–70, but they were still extremely scarce in Lower Silesia, where only three colonies were known in 1970. After then their expansion took off, and by 1981, when they were still increasing, they were common throughout most of the region, although still very scarce in the coastal area.

In the former Soviet Union, Fieldfares have spread south and west during this century. Although there is little information, a decline has been reported in areas such as south of Moscow and in Gorky. Similarly, they are said to have decreased lately as breeding birds in Estonia and Latvia.

In the country known until recently as Czechoslovakia, the Fieldfare was already established as a widespread breeding bird in the north of Bohemia and Moravia by the middle of the nineteenth century. Further expansion occurred in waves: in 1860–80 Bohemia was completely colonized, and the years 1880–1910 saw a push into middle Moravia. Slovakia was first reached in 1882–87, but there were only sporadic occurrences until the 1950s, when the species became more established. In

1972–74 there was a clear expansion in east Slovakia, when Fieldfares populated the valleys of the Poprad, Torysa and Hornad, and finally, near Košice, the north-east border of Hungary. In the Czech Republic today, Fieldfares are almost ubiquitous breeders, with small gaps in the Elbe lowlands and some larger gaps in south Moravia and also in the south and east of the Slovak Republic.

The late nineteenth century expansion of breeding range in the area now in the Czech and Slovak Republics was not echoed farther south, and there was only a single record of Fieldfares breeding in Austria, in 1887. There were short-lived colonization attempts from 1910 onwards in a variety of Austrian sites, until World War II saw a spread from south Bohemia to the granite plateaux of Upper Austria. From 1946 to 1955 it established a number of isolated breeding sites there, and then from 1955 onwards, spread out more or less simultaneously from these centres.

By 1978, the western provinces of Vorarlberg, Tyrol and Salzburg were almost entirely colonized, as was most of Upper Austria, although Fieldfares were still scarce in the central part, and in Lower Austria there are still only isolated breeding sites. As well as the apparently unbroken trend of population increase in Austria, there has been a remarkable advance to greater heights in the alpine regions. The highest known breeding place in the eastern Alps was at 1300 m in 1966, but by 1977 the species had bred at 1780 m, and in 1984 it reached 2310 m. The expansion in range is now most obvious in Styria and Carinthia, where colonies have reached the Lower Austrian border at Semmering and the Slovenian border near Bleiburg. In Slovenia, breeding was first discovered in 1975 in the valley of Sava Dolinka, in the far north-west ; further records were forthcoming the following year, on Ljubljana Marsh and up to 80 km away at Ilirska Bistrica, and since then the species has spread south-eastwards and become more frequent and regular in Slovenia.

Fieldfares were found breeding in Greece in the early 1980s, and just across the border in Macedonia in 1986. Aristotle, a keen observer of matters biological, noted that 'thrushes make nests like swallows out of mud in the tops of trees, in rows and close together, forming a kind of chain'. Although Blackbirds and Song Thrushes will use mud to form their nests, the colony description fits only the Fieldfare and suggests that it may have bred in ancient Greece. The recent nests in that region are unprecedentedly far south for modern times, but were – typically for Fieldfares – at fairly high altitude, in the hills over 1000 m above sea level.

In Hungary, Fieldfares have nested since 1947 in the Hanság area near the Austrian and Slovak borders, and in 1977 they colonized the southern foothills of the Mátra range north-east of Budapest. In recent times they have increased in northern Hungary, this probably connected with their spread in Slovakia. Fieldfares have also spread to Romania, and are continuing to extend their range in recent years. They first nested in 1966 near Suceava in the eastern Carpathian mountains, some 70 km from the Ukraine border, and in 1968–71 colonised other sites in the region, westwards towards Vatra Dornei. By 1972–73, they had spread to breed in the southern foothills of the Maramures mountains and at two sites in the upper reaches of the river Muresul in Transylvania. In 1975 they were

A Fieldfare in autumn, recently arrived on the English east coast, feeding on Sea-buckthorn. This bird is an obvious first-year, with light-coloured fringes to the coverts clearly visible.

found 250 km to the south, near Cimpulung, in 1979 two pairs nested near Brasov, and two years later Fieldfares bred near Sibiu, these localities being in the southern Carpathian chain. In 1983, a loose colony near Brasov, said to be the third colony found in the country, held fourteen occupied nests in an area of 8 km^2.

The Fieldfare's breeding areas in Italy are mainly in the subalpine far north, but with scattered outposts elsewhere. After summering records from 1936, breeding was suspected in Trento in 1963 and first proven in 1968 in Brescia. Records quickly followed from Sienna and Bolzano and by 1975 they had spread swiftly through much of the south Tyrol and Aosta regions to breed widely in the regions bordering Austria, Friuli and Trentino, with a few farther west in Lombardy and Piedmont. Their range is still increasing in the Alps.

At the other extreme, a flourishing colony of Fieldfares was found in south Greenland (close to 60°N) in 1947, probably having been established ten years previously when strong south-easterly winds in January 1937 carried birds way out of their normal range. By 1951, they had spread to nest extensively in a fairly large area of the southern part of Greenland, adding a new breeding species to the Nearctic fauna. The Greenland population, apparently resident and self-sustaining, was nearly wiped out by the snowy winter of 1966/67. Since then, breeding was proven near Narssarssuaq until at least 1975 and in Julianehåb District until 1979, but I have not been able to trace any later references.

Fieldfares used to be very scarce in Iceland, with single specimens obtained in the spring of 1823, and on 6 December 1885, 15 December 1894 and in December 1900. In the first decade of the twentieth century they were observed six or seven times, and in the following 25 years increased gradually. Since about 1930 they occurred annually in small flocks in the Vestmann Islands. They were found much more frequently in 1938–43 and became a regular winter visitor to most parts of Iceland, occurring in flocks of 2–20 birds, occasionally in swarms of 100–200 individuals, and usually disappearing between the end of March and late April. However, they did not start breeding in Iceland until the time of the 10th International Ornithological Congress in Uppsala (10–17 June 1950), by chance at exactly the time when Dr Gudmundsson presented his paper predicting that the Fieldfare would soon be added to the island's list of breeding birds. This was expected as a continuation of the climatic change that had led to breeding in Iceland in the first half of the twentieth century by a number of southern species including Starling (1935), Short-eared Owl (1928), Shoveler (1931), Tufted Duck (before 1900), Black-headed Gull (1911), Herring Gull (1920–30) and Lesser Black-backed Gull (1920–30). Species that have also bred, but not become established, include Swallow (1911) and Coot (once in 1891, next in 1943).

Although Fieldfares have only recently colonized Iceland, Redwings have been breeding there long enough to have evolved as a different subspecies (*Turdus iliacus coburni*), slightly larger and darker than the Scandinavian birds. Fieldfares are not fully established as Icelandic breeders, the only recent records being of two pairs in 1982 and one pair in 1990.

It is clear that the species has undergone a spectacular extension in range in continental Europe during the twentieth century, apparently relentless and without suffering any retreat. In summarizing this spread, however, it would be misleading to give the impression that the movement has been continuous. For instance, in 1977, a group of nests was found in Champagne, 100 km west of the nearest known colony near Nancy, and in

The Fieldfare's typical pose on the ground, looking alert and rather upright, with the bill pointing slightly upwards.

1982 a pair bred in Prater Park, Vienna, 150 km from the nearest other site. Similarly, the species' breeding sites in Britain have been separated from each other by hundreds of kilometres.

Breeding in Britain

A nest and three newly fledged young were found in Orkney in 1967, the first recorded breeding by Fieldfares in the British Isles. They probably bred also in Co. Durham in 1967, a pair and three juveniles being seen in mid-July. They bred again in Orkney in 1969 and 1974 and possibly in other years as well. Nesting has been confirmed in Shetland, annually from 1968 to 1971 and in 1973, 1974, 1982, 1983 and 1992.

On the Scottish mainland, Fieldfares first nested in Inverness in 1970, also breeding there in 1982, 1986 and 1987, and breeding has been proven in the counties of Banff (1972 and 1989), Kincardine (1973), Grampian (1976, 1977 and 1990), Perth (1979) and Sutherland (1983 and 1990) and suspected in Caithness, Ross, Mull and Selkirk. The colonization of Scotland, however, has been slow and patchy, with not more than two pairs confirmed breeding in any one year.

Lingering spring birds had long raised speculation that the species might nest in England, and indeed breeding was proven in Derbyshire in 1969, 1970, 1974, 1975, 1978, 1980, 1981 and 1989. In 1974, a pair in north Staffordshire reared four young and another pair may also have bred; the breeding success there was repeated in 1975, when a pair nested little more than a metre from the 1974 site and another probably bred, and Fieldfares bred in Staffordshire also in 1976, 1977 and 1985.

Odd birds frequented other parts of the Peak District and breeding was proven in 1976 and 1980 in South Yorkshire, and probable in West Yorkshire in 1982 and 1983, when adults and juveniles were seen feeding with Mistle Thrushes in July and August. Young were probably reared at two sites in Cumbria in 1977, and adults have been seen in suitable habitat in the county in later years. From 1976 onwards, summering individuals have been seen in various counties in southern England, including Bedfordshire, Buckinghamshire, Suffolk, Essex, Kent and East Sussex, and in West Glamorgan and Powys in Wales, and in the Isle of Man in 1989, although none was proved to breed as judged by the strict standards of the Rare Breeding Birds Panel. The English counties in which breeding has recently been proven are Berkshire (1988), Yorkshire (1990) and Northumberland (1988 and 1990).

There are two populations that could equally well have supplied the colonizers of Britain: those breeding to the north of the Baltic (in Fennoscandia) and those of north-central Europe. The first few British breeding records, from Scotland, presumably involved birds from Scandinavia, parallelling for instance the spread of Redwing and Wood Sandpiper. However, Robert Spencer, in his chapter 'Our changing avifauna' in Hickling's book *Enjoying Ornithology*, published in 1983 to celebrate the 50th anniversary of the founding of the BTO, suggests that later records of Fieldfares breeding in counties such as Derbyshire and, of summering birds seen in Kent, Suffolk and elsewhere in southern England must almost certainly represent a continuation by southern stock of their westward push across north-central Europe. So far, the discussion of the origins of the British colonists must remain speculation, but measurements of the birds and their nests may help, since birds from northern stock tend to be larger and to build deeper nests.

In Britain, the species is on the edge of its continental range, and the authors of *Red Data Birds in Britain* (Batten *et al.* 1991) considered it likely that it may slowly expand its range in Britain, possibly with small-scale contractions in some years. At present there is no sign of regular breeding in any particular area, or of a colony becoming established. All of the British birds have nested solitarily, but the first sign of a colonial habit was in 1992 when two active nests were found within 10 m of each other.

Although breeding in Britain has been annual since 1967, never more than a few nests have been built in any year. The totals of breeding pairs in the five years 1973–77 were only 2–3, 3–7, 2–10, 3–12 and 4–6 respectively. Since then the expected colonization has faltered, with the next four years (1978–81) having 1–4, 1–6, 1–5 and 0–6 pairs. Later figures fluctuated somewhat, with 1982–89 totals of 2–7, 3–12, 0–4, 0–3, 2, 1–7, 2–7 and 3–13 pairs. The year 1990, with five pairs proved breeding, and another seven possibles, was the best yet for Fieldfares in the U.K. Their growth and spread appears hesitant, however, especially when compared with that on the Continent, in the Netherlands, Belgium, Luxembourg and France. The British breeding distribution is strangely fragmented, with odd pairs nesting hundreds of kilometres distant from the nearest others. Such habits make it well-nigh impossible to organize a coordinated census, and isolated pairs could have bred undetected almost anywhere in Britain.

Fieldfares have not yet bred in Ireland, the latest record of birds lingering in spring being of two in Galway on 3 June 1978. The only July records are of singles near Dublin on 14 July 1914 and 21 July 1965.

Non-breeding range

So long as food is available, Fieldfares can endure, and survive, the rigours of an Arctic winter. They have been seen on the Norwegian highlands in a temperature of −30°C, and every year some Fieldfares remain to winter in southern Finland, southern Sweden and along the south and west coasts of Norway south of 65°N. Within Russia, if food proves sufficient, they winter as far north as St Petersburg and right across Siberia to Perm, Tomsk and Krasnoyarsk (56°N, 93°E). In most years, some reach the North Atlantic islands of the Faroes and Iceland, with odd movements to Greenland, and sporadically they are found in North America. The Fieldfare's normal winter range includes the British Isles and almost all of Continental Europe as far south as the north of the Iberian peninsula, northern Italy and the Balkans and thence across to the coasts of the Ukrainian Black Sea and the Caucasus range in Georgia and Azerbaijan. From there they are regularly found in southern Turkmenia, across to Samarkand in Uzbekistan, also wintering in sheltered valleys in mountainous Tadzhikistan. The Fieldfare's wintering status in Kazakhstan is uncertain. Around Lake Tengiz, west of Karaganda, it has been recorded only up to mid-December and in March. In

Hard weather drives many Fieldfares into suburban gardens, where they gorge themselves on any berries they can find.

the region of the Ili delta, flowing into Lake Balkhash, it was seen, in small numbers, in only three out of ten winters from the mid-1950s onwards. Farther south, in Kirghizia, it regularly winters in the forests of pistachio trees mixed with conifers, while the valley of the Chulyshman river in the Altai mountains holds large flocks of wintering birds.

Small numbers of Fieldfares are often found in winter to the south of this general line, with odd birds moving out of Europe into Africa and Asia Minor and some of the Asian breeding stock moving to winter in China. Occasional individuals have been seen in the Canaries, Madeira, the Arabian peninsula, India and Japan. Some are found in winter in the central European and west Siberian breeding areas, but mostly these are immigrants from farther north, the local breeders having moved out. It seems that, in all populations, those that stay put for the winter are very much in the minority, and most birds migrate, usually to the south-west or south-east, vast numbers then appearing in areas where they do not breed.

The *Atlas of Wintering Birds in Britain and Ireland*, for which the fieldwork was conducted from mid-November to February in the three winters of 1981/82, 1982/83 and 1983/84, showed Fieldfares to be widespread in large numbers, except in the highlands and the bleakest coastal areas of north-west Scotland. The densest concentrations were along the southern coastal counties of England, from Kent to Devon, and then northwards in a broad swathe through the West Midlands as far as

Cheshire, with local abundances elsewhere in South Yorkshire, Northumberland and the central lowlands of Scotland. They were noticeably thinner on the ground in Cornwall, east Anglia and Wales. Trying to analyse the environmental factors determining their distribution, it is clear that, in general, they avoided the coldest areas (with mean January temperatures below about 3.5°C) and the areas with highest rainfall; they were much less likely to be found in numbers on moorland or the higher-lying areas, certainly those above 2500 ft (760 m), but also shunning most of those over 1000 ft (300 m) above sea level. Of course, several of these factors are linked, and it is not obvious which are most important for Fieldfares in winter. They can be very mobile, with massive flocks on the move to avoid harsh weather (see Chapters 7 and 8), and their winter distribution always contains an element of unpredictability.

In Scotland, Valerie Thom (1986) noted that the first arrivals sometimes appear in August and may consist largely of young birds. Numbers are seldom high until October, when the main influx generally occurs. This varies greatly between years, with some seasons having successive waves of several thousands at a time moving across the country, and others with few flocks of more than a thousand reported. Peak counts at Fair Isle have ranged from 100 to 8000. Large numbers occur at times on the east coast, where an exceptional 33,000 were estimated near the Ythan estuary on 26 October 1980, but also passing south inland. In years of major invasions sizeable numbers reach the Hebrides, where Fieldfares are normally much scarcer than Redwings. Many of the birds found in autumn in Scotland apparently move on to Ireland or England, and some as far as France, but some stay throughout the winter. Scattered small flocks are seen in the Highlands in most winters, a few occasionally remain in Shetland and Orkney, and there are wintering records in Speyside, but most Scottish wintering records are in the lowlands.

Clive Hutchinson (1989) wrote that Redwings and Song Thrushes are numerous in Ireland, but Fieldfares are far less common. Irish totals tend to increase after December, with birds moving from Britain, and exceptional numbers are sometimes found when hard weather strikes farther east. They were found in the wintering atlas survey of 1981/82 to 1983/84 throughout most of the country, being absent only from parts of west Donegal, west Galway and Mayo, and the highest parts of the Wicklow mountains. The largest numbers were east of the Shannon, contrary to the traditional view that Fieldfares are more abundant in the west. Large flocks are not infrequent on the east coast, particularly after cold weather, but the largest recorded assemblies in Ireland tend to be of 1000 – 1500 birds, much smaller than the maxima occasionally found in Britain. Only 9 per cent of the Irish 10 x 10 km squares fell into the category of more than 500 birds seen in a day, compared with 24 per cent of the British squares.

To the north, Fieldfares regularly reach the Faroes in autumn, some of them remaining to winter there. Similarly, some reach Iceland in most years, from late September onwards, and a Fieldfare ringed in northern Norway in June 1959 was found in Iceland in November. The largest recent count is of a flock of over 300 present for a week (20–27 November 1982) at Húsavík in north-east Iceland, with a total of at least 530 on the island then. Some birds stay until the end of April/early May, and now and again odd ones remain to breed. Fieldfares have been recorded travelling far out into the Atlantic, with flocks seen from weather ships 890 km due west of Orkney (south of Iceland), but farther north and west the species used to be very scarce. A flock was seen on Jan Mayen on 4–5 May 1883, of which four were shot; a male was shot in Godthåb district, west Greenland, on 24 November 1925, and another (unsexed) shot at Angmagssalik, east Greenland, on 1 December 1935.

Then, in the middle of January 1937, a large flock of Fieldfares crossed the North Atlantic. Their provenance has been carefully analysed and it is considered that they were likely to have been birds that had stayed most of the winter in southern Scandinavia, probably coastal Norway, and were stimulated to leave by inadequate food supplies and persistent, cold, south-easterly winds. This season was notable for large eruptions of Fieldfares over northern Eurasia. The temperature dropped suddenly in the afternoon of 19 January and may have triggered their migration. If they set off in the usual south-westerly direction, towards the British Isles, the strong winds would have carried them way off course, towards north-east Greenland, at about 100 km per hour. In the dark they probably lost their orientation and within 15 – 20 hours were carried north of the Arctic Circle. The flock was first traced on Jan Mayen, where several birds arrived on 20 January, and one was picked up and skinned. At the same time a Norwegian trapper secured an adult male specimen on Ymer Island in north-east Greenland.

It is amazing to recall that in January it is dark 24 hours a day at these latitudes (73°N). In the last days of the month the irruption reached south-west Greenland and several were seen or shot in Godthåb District on 27 January. They were seen into the first few days of February but later disappeared. When Dr Finn Salomonsen visited Godthåb in 1946, nine years later, he found that the Greenlanders well remembered this peculiar invasion of birds which were completely unknown to them. The majority of the Fieldfares hurried to the south along the west coast of Greenland, reaching close to the southern tip in Julianehåb District, where four males were shot during 28 – 31 January.

Parts of the irrupting flocks may have continued to Arctic North America. This is not certain, but a semi-mummified skin was found in the possession of an old Eskimo woman at Jens Munk Island (69°30'N, 80°W), at the head of Foxe Basin, in 1939, with its date of taking uncertain. This was said to be the first for North America, although there is a record from Connecticut in April 1878. One was seen in Ottawa, Canada, in January 1967. Another was found, and also claimed to be the first for the American continent, on 15 June 1968, at Point Barrow, Alaska: this was a male that had been dead for one to two weeks.

The species is now a casual visitor to Canada, with others, following the Ottawa bird of 1967, in Nova Scotia in October 1971 and October 1972 and in Newfoundland in January 1973. One was ringed at Long Point, Ontario, on 24 May 1975, one stayed in Quebec from 4 January to 14 March 1976, with another in Ontario in January/February 1981 and another in Quebec in spring 1985. One was in Delaware from 30 March to 4 April 1969, with other American records from New York State in February 1983, Alaska on 9 June 1982 and in spring 1985, and

Massachusetts in spring 1986. A Fieldfare in Minnesota, the first for the mid-west of the continent, arrived following a snowstorm and was present from 3 – 10 November 1991. It is intriguing that several of the North American records have been in spring: one wonders where these birds passed the winter.

Fieldfares are accidental on Bear Island, and have been irregularly found on Spitsbergen (Svalbard) at over 77°N, the farthest north they have been recorded.

Large numbers are found wintering in most countries of Continental Europe. The Dutch year-round atlas reports high concentrations of Fieldfares in November in the areas of the dunes and orchards, reflecting their preferences for berries, particularly of Sea-buckthorn, and apples. From October to March they are widespread, found in over 85 per cent of the country, and in over 90 per cent in November – February.

Flocks of several hundreds to several thousands are frequently noted in France in winter. They are very widespread, almost ubiquitous, but become sparsely distributed in the south-west of the country, roughly west of the Rhone and south of the river Dordogne, where they were present in only about half of the possible squares in the winter atlas survey in 1977–81. This is the area with the highest hunting pressure, but no explanation for the distribution is offered by the authors of the French winter atlas.

In Germany, Fieldfares are widespread in most winters, especially in the milder northern half of the country. For instance, flocks of 400–2200 were found in Lübcke's study area in Hessen from the beginning of November to the end of March.

They are common winter visitors to Austria in moderate numbers. Noteworthy flocks of up to 7000 were commented upon in the east of the country, in Burgenland province, in the second half of December 1978.

Northern Spain as a rule has its earliest Fieldfares at the end of October, with a peak in December. The number of winter visitors varies from year to year. Some reach the northern half of Portugal in most winters; flocks are occasionally found in open country south of the river Tagus, but normally only when the winter is particularly harsh elsewhere in Europe. Similarly, the wintering numbers on the Balearic islands of Mallorca, Minorca and Ibiza depend entirely on the weather farther north. In Gibraltar, Fieldfares are scarce migrants, the Strait being at the southern end of their wintering range; one Finnish-ringed bird was recovered in December, but the main months of passage are October, and February and March.

In Malta the Fieldfare is known as *Malvizza tal-qtajja*, and is a scarce passage migrant and winter visitor in irregular numbers from late October to mid-March, although one was once seen in late August. The birds are usually found in small flocks of up to twelve, with 'large numbers' in winter 1873/74. Such major influxes tend to be noticed especially in areas with a tradition of hunting, as in Italy, where exceptional numbers were present in the winters of 1936/37, 1952/53 and 1965/66. Most Italian records are from the north of the country. On the island of Corsica, Fieldfares are only occasionally seen. In Sicily they are described as a scarce to locally fairly common winter visitor in highly variable numbers, from November to February, but mostly December-January, with one record in late March; they are usually found singly or in small flocks of up to 50, but local influxes of hundreds have sometimes been reported.

Some Fieldfares reach Africa. In some years they invade North Africa in considerable numbers and are generally found along the Mediterranean coast and the Nile Delta, but have also been observed in Wadi Natroun (30°20'N, 30°20'E) and elsewhere in lower Egypt. In Egypt, where they are called *Duj al-ghayt*, they are fairly common in some years, on dates from 18 September to 14 March, and in others completely absent. They have reached as far south as Sohag and the region of Luxor, but this species has not been recorded in the Sudan. Farther west, Fieldfares are perhaps more sporadic in Libya, with extreme dates of 28 October to 6 March.

There are odd records of twos or threes in November inland in the Cyrenaica region of east Libya. Farther along the coast, the first record in Tunisia was in March 1866, with the next in winter 1965/66 when they were common in the north, flocks of up to 50 being found near the Libyan border (this was also a year with record numbers wintering in Italy). There is an old report from the Algerian coast, at the end of February in 1906, but to date only four records in total in Algeria, one of which had been ringed in Italy. Rather more might be expected in Morocco, with the possibility of crossing from Iberia, and a flock of 18 birds was seen just south of the Gibraltar strait in spring 1892, but the two found in the Middle Atlas mountains on 7 January 1984 constituted only the eighth Moroccan sighting of the species on record.

Fieldfares have occasionally been found in the Canary Islands and Madeira in winter. This is odd, since they are so scarce in Africa. Even odder are the several records from the Canaries in spring, and it is difficult to imagine where these birds have come from.

At the east end of the Mediterranean, there appears to be no information in the literature on the status of the Fieldfare in Albania although some must winter there as sizeable flocks are found in all regions of the former Yugoslavia and in Greece. They are quite common winter visitors to Bulgaria. The Fieldfare is a winter visitor to Cyprus in variable numbers in scrub and wooded areas on high and low ground. It is particularly fond of feeding on berries of the Strawberry Tree in the hills. The birds are usually found in flocks of tens to hundreds, with the largest on record being 'many thousands' at Akrotiri in December 1970. They were once seen in mid-September, but the first arrivals usually occur from late October to November, with the peak in December-January, markedly fewer in February, and only occasional singles from March to mid-April. In Turkey, they are winter vagrants to the Anatolian plateau, where up to 1000 were found on 26 March 1946. P.A. Buxton studied the birds of Iran just after World War I and found Fieldfares to be common in the forest near Rasht (on the south edge of the Caspian Sea) in winter; the latest were in Juniper bushes at 8000 ft (2400 m) in the hills above Menjil on 27 March. They have been recorded in Syria, Jordan, Lebanon (where a Finnish-ringed individual was found in winter 1965/66), and they are annual in Israel, with a flock of 100 once at Eilat; the earliest are usually at the end of October, with peak numbers in December or January, and odd birds as late as March or April. The Fieldfare was added to the Iraqi list in

1956, and is now known to winter there in small numbers, varying from year to year. It is accidental in Kuwait, and in the United Arab Emirates has been found very rarely, but never in Oman, and I have not been able to trace any other records of Fieldfares in the Arabian peninsula.

In Asia, Fieldfares have been found in Afghanistan, and there is one undated record from Uttar Pradesh in northern India, presumably a bird of the mid- to east-Siberian form, but the species is not mentioned in recent avifaunas of Nepal or Pakistan. From looking at the rest of their range, it seems that Fieldfares must visit Mongolia, but they are unrecorded there. They are found in winter in the north-west of China (the provinces of Kansu, Tsinghai, and the Tien Shan uplands in Sinkiang) and are rare visitors to north-east China. In Japan, where the Fieldfare is called *Nohara-tsugumi*, there are three records, all from central Honshu: single birds were found frequenting rural country, with rice and vegetable fields close to woodland, in January 1960, February 1988 and February-March 1989.

Population

It is a fact of life that far more people are interested in studying the rare and unusual than the commonplace. Many birdwatchers will go to exceptional lengths to see the first one, but are not interested in the next thousand, or million. Thus, small populations are recorded in detail, while the larger ones are not well known. Of course, it is much easier to count a few colonies than to carry out a quantitative breeding census of an entire country, but this does mean that there is little idea of the world Fieldfare population. A further problem with this species is that absolute counts of the population are difficult in view of large fluctuations from year to year: this is characteristic of its breeding strategy, with high mortality and a high reproductive rate.

Even experienced ornithologists sometimes cannot agree on population figures. The Ornithological Association in Bonn has estimated a West German population figure of 110,000 breeding pairs, while the Bodensee branch of the same association came up with a figure of 3,000,000 pairs, both presumably extrapolating from the local density in their region. The latter value is now known to be far too high, and I guess that one million may be realistic for the whole of the unified Germany, with an area of about 360,000 km^2 and an average density of 3 pairs/km^2.

In Sweden, there were an estimated 1,500,000 breeding pairs of Fieldfares in 1976, the figure of 15 million given in *Birds of the Western Palearctic* presumably being a misprint for this figure. The totals for the rest of the thrush family in Sweden are 1,500,000 pairs of Blackbirds (the same as Fieldfare), with Song Thrush the most numerous at 3,500,000 pairs, and 1,000,000 Redwings, 200,000 Mistle Thrushes and 5000 Ring Ouzels.

In Finland, Fieldfares, with an estimated 560,000 pairs, were the sixth most frequent breeding species in 1972, behind Redwing and Song Thrush. There has been a well-documented steady increase in the Finnish breeding population, with a slight decline from 1926 to 1949 followed by an increase of about fourfold from then to 1977. I have not been able to find a published figure for Norway, but it must be similar to the Swedish total: the area of the country is rather less, but the breeding density of Fieldfares may be higher, bearing in mind the massive concentrations on the west coast. The Scandinavian total must be close to 3–3.5 million breeding pairs.

Turning now to some of the well-studied smaller populations, the Belgian breeding population has undergone explosive growth: after the first nest was found in 1967, an estimate just fifteen years later was of 10,000 pairs. The Dutch population has also expanded rapidly. After the first recent proven breeding record, of one pair in 1972, the next five years saw totals of 1–2, 3–6, 15–20, 30–45 and 54–75 pairs probably breeding, of which 1, 1, 12, 29 and 27 respectively were proven. Censuses in their south Limburg stronghold showed a big increase, from 20–21 pairs in 1975–77 to 218–294 pairs in 1981: in 1982 there were 261–304 pairs, and in 1983, 343–351 pairs. Although bad weather in spring 1984 delayed their arrival in their breeding areas, the population rose further to 516–531 pairs. By 1990 there were over 700 pairs breeding in the Netherlands. The population in France was said to be under 10,000 pairs at the time of the breeding-bird atlas (1976), and is undoubtedly somewhat higher now.

Western Europe probably holds around 5 million pairs of Fieldfares, at a mean density of about 3 pairs/km^2. I have not seen any published figure for the world population. The total area over which the species breeds is perhaps 10,000,000 km^2, and the mean density might be 1–2 pairs/ km^2, thus giving a world breeding population of 10–20 million pairs, but this estimate is dominated by the assumptions made about the area and density of the stock – largely unknown – of the vast countries of the former Soviet Union, particularly Russia, Kazakhstan and Ukraine. If the higher end of this speculative range of figures is correct, then at the end of a good breeding season, there may be 60 million Fieldfares in the world.

If counts of breeding populations are difficult, at least breeding birds are fixed to a site for a couple of months, whereas the species' mobility outside the breeding season makes counts of wintering birds almost impracticable. When there was a rich supply of Rowan berries in the district of Olbernhau in the Erz mountains of eastern Germany in mid-winter 1985/86, there were large flocks of Fieldfares amounting to an estimated 110,000 birds in an area of 160 km^2. In Ossetia, in the subalpine Caucasus, a wintering density averaging 4 birds/ km^2 has been suggested. David Snow (1986) gave a very tentative figure for Britain and Ireland, from the maps for the wintering atlas, of about 1,000,000 birds, with the strong caveat that movements within any one winter make it almost impossible to derive a more precise figure.

3

FOOD AND FEEDING

Fieldfares have been recorded as taking a very wide range of food, and feeding in many different ways. Most descriptions, however, apply to extreme circumstances when their favoured foods are unavailable, and merely show how adaptable the species can be when hardpressed. They usually tend to feed on invertebrates taken from the open fields, and also on fruit, found mainly in hedgerows. They do not normally frequent heavily wooded areas except when they come down to feed on apples in orchards, a favourite food in hard weather. Fieldfares show a very marked association with permanent grass fields, and strongly avoid stubble, bare till, winter-cereal fields or leys (temporary grass or clover).

Pioneering work on bird feeding was carried out just after World War I by Collinge, who was interested mainly in their economic effects on agriculture. He classed the food taken as 'injurious' or 'beneficial',

OPPOSITE *Rowan berries are Fieldfares' favourite food in Scandinavia in the autumn and early winter (above). A Fieldfare often tilts its head to one side while apparently listening for earthworms, their most important summer food (below).*
BELOW *An alert-looking adult in winter, surrounded by apples.*

depending on whether the prey items were harmful or helpful to farmers. He examined the stomach and intestine of 30 shot Fieldfares over the entire wintering period in Britain (September to May), and reported their diet to comprise 59 per cent invertebrates (37 per cent insects, 15% per cent earthworms, 4 per cent slugs, 3 per cent others) and 41 per cent vegetable matter (36 per cent wild fruits and seeds, 5 per cent other plant material). Collinge proclaimed 41.5 per cent of the Fieldfare's choice of food to be 'injurious' (adult beetles and the larvae of beetles, dipterous flies and Lepidoptera, slugs, spiders, millipedes, woodlice), 2 per cent 'neutral' and only 1 per cent 'beneficial', leading to his conclusion that 'this is a most valuable bird to the farmer, and certainly merits every protection during its stay in this country.'

Fieldfares take a wide range of invertebrates, mostly the slow-moving ones. Their recorded diet in the West Palearctic has included dragonflies, crickets, bugs, scorpion flies, larval Lepidoptera (butterflies and moths), adults and larvae of flies, Hymenoptera (bees and wasps), and beetles, and full-grown weevils, spiders, harvestmen, millipedes, snails, slugs, earthworms and leeches.

In a study in southern Norway, 62 stomachs from birds collected in both spring and autumn contained mainly invertebrates. In spring, the invertebrates were mostly earthworms and adult beetles, with numerous ants, and the plant foods mainly berries of heaths (mainly Cowberry) and Juniper. In autumn, the invertebrates were largely beetles (mostly adults), harvestmen and ants, with the vegetable material almost entirely berries, especially from Crowberry, heaths and Rowan. As might be expected, the biggest variety of animal and plant foods was found in autumn.

Fifteen stomachs of Fieldfares collected near Moscow in June and July contained 97 items comprising 36 per cent (by number) beetles, 15 per cent Hymenoptera, 14 per cent Lepidoptera larvae, 6 per cent Diptera (mainly larvae), 5.5 per cent earthworms, 4.5 per cent centipedes, 5 per cent other invertebrates and 14 per cent plant material. The low proportion of earthworms is surprising, compared with a study in the summer in southern Norway, where earthworms made up, on average, 60 per cent by weight of food in the stomachs of breeding adults in woodland colonies adjoining pastures; of the rest, beetles comprised 10 per cent (larvae and adults), with a few other invertebrates and 20 per cent brown vegetation. Earthworms were clearly very important for the breeding females, so much so that the mean egg weight in a Norwegian colony depended on the biomass of worms in the birds' feeding areas. Later on, when the eggs hatched, these Norwegian birds made a clear distinction between what they ate themselves and what they fed to their chicks; the adults took no beetles or snails to their young, and gave them an even higher proportion of worms than they ate themselves.

Song Thrushes are renowned for using an anvil to break snails. This behaviour has been rarely recorded for Fieldfares, but is described by Lübcke and Furrer (1985). Eating snails probably provides calcium as well as energy.

In Sweden, Fieldfares usually forage in grassy meadows. In the north, the most frequented feeding sites are south-facing valleys and mountain slopes with scattered trees, bushes and grassland. In south-west Sweden, tilled fields and cultivated land together with wet areas attract feeding Fieldfares.

Fieldfares feed either in small scattered flocks or as individuals. They may defend temporary feeding territories, both in and out of the breeding season, but they generally roam a feeding site as a loose flock, each bird foraging individually. Fieldfares typically forage by moving in short rushes made up of one or more hops or steps. In between rushes, they pause and move their heads and bodies, apparently scanning the area. If a potential prey item is spotted, the bird either takes a few paces towards it or attacks it immediately. Birds frequently crouch low over the grass before attacking, but often they crouch forward without subsequently moving in for the kill. Worms are caught by probing, with a vigorous stab into the ground. In a detailed study in Sweden, 37 per cent of such probing attacks succeeded in getting prey. Surface items like larvae or adult insects are caught by swift snatches at the grass or pecks, which were more successful, 58 per cent resulting in prey being obtained. In a typical minute, the average Fieldfare had 8.1 stops, 1.3 probes, 0.75 snatches/ pecks and 2.5 crouches. Small worms, up to 37 mm long, typically took only a second to extract from the ground, with another few seconds to manipulate them into the carrying position, but the longest worms (>137 mm) took an average of eight seconds to pull out and over a minute of handling time.

The difference between the feeding methods of Fieldfares and Redwings was carefully studied in Cambridgeshire by Alan Tye. Fieldfares in winter (to mid-February) took 44 per cent of their food items (all less than 10 mm long) from the surface, and 56 per cent from in the soil, whereas with Redwings the proportions were 67 per cent and 33 per cent. Only 22 per cent of the Redwings' soil items were larger than 10 mm, while 45 per cent of Fieldfares' were. The 'surface' items were flies, beetles and spiders,

Earthworms are Fieldfares' main summer food. Long worms may take a few seconds to pull out, and over a minute to manipulate into position and swallow.

with the 'soil' items being earthworms, centipedes, slugs, and larvae of beetles and craneflies. Similar methods were used by both species for similar types of prey, but there were some differences in foraging behaviour, with Redwings regularly searching cowpats and leaf litter whereas Fieldfares never used cowpats and seldom investigated leaf litter. In late February and March, when bigger surface items started to become available, Fieldfares took more surface items then (75 per cent of their food items). This suggests that prey size is what determines the Fieldfares' use of soil-digging techniques; they are larger birds and need bigger prey.

Studies of flocks of wintering thrushes in fields in the English Midlands showed that single-species flocks of Fieldfares and Redwings tended to occur on different types of pasture, with Fieldfares on new (less than four years old) and Redwings on old (25-400 years old). Worms were less abundant on new pasture but were apparently easier to detect. Comparing single-species flocks of Fieldfares on old or new pastures, they had significantly higher rates of prey capture on new pasture, and a slightly higher net energy intake there. They gained energy more quickly in larger flocks, where they spent less time scanning around for predators, and more time crouching, searching for food. The value of pausing to crouch was illustrated by the finding that bigger worms were taken after a bird had crouched than if it just pounced without crouching first.

Mixed flocks of Fieldfares and Redwings were almost always formed by the former joining an existing flock of the latter on old pasture. On old pasture, both species had higher net rates of energy intake in mixed flocks than in single-species flocks. Fieldfares took bigger worms in mixed flocks, and it is suggested that they use clues from the Redwings about the location of prey, although it is not known how they do this.

Quantitative studies of food in winter are sometimes contradictory. Fieldfares visiting Hungary took animal prey until 3 November and from March to mid-May, comprising beetles, snails, grasshoppers and Hemiptera; no Lepidoptera, Diptera or Hymenoptera were found in the stomach analyses. Old records of 94 Fieldfares examined in Hungary between 8 November and 9 April, however, revealed 245 invertebrate prey items, adults or larvae, 77 per cent of which were beetles, 7 per cent Lepidoptera, 3 per cent millipedes, 3 per cent spiders, 3 per cent Hemiptera, 1 per cent grasshoppers and 6 per cent molluscs. From their autumn arrival in Bulgaria they were said to eat mainly insects, usually beetles and ants; in winter, insects were still found but in restricted variety, with ants being the most common, while in March there was a considerable increase in snails and beetles with a corresponding fall in the number of ants eaten.

Fieldfares have been recorded feeding on a very wide variety of vegetable matter. *The Birds of the Western Palearctic* lists them as taking the fruit or seeds of Juniper, Yew, pinks, Mistletoe, Barberry, Bramble (blackberries), strawberry, rose, Rowan, cherries, apple, pear, *Cotoneaster*, currant, Hawthorn, Bilberry (Whortleberry), Crowberry, Elder, Buckthorn, Sea-buckthorn, Snowberry, vine, Holly, sedges and grasses; and also the shoots of grasses, buds of alder and buds and catkins of birch. Lübcke and Furrer compiled an even longer list, including also Sycamore, Ivy, Shadbush, Honeysuckle (Woodbine), Raspberry, Virginia Creeper, Gean

(Wild Cherry), Bird Cherry, privet, Cranberry, Oleaster, Spindle Tree, Dewberry, Cloudberry, Cowberry, Blackthorn (Sloe), Guelder Rose, Gooseberry, Small-leaved Lime and plum. Fieldfares have recently been noted feeding on *Viburnum* during a snowy winter. They even eat the berries of Mezereon, which is poisonous to man, and there are reports of people becoming ill after eating Fieldfares that had consumed these seeds.

Despite this long list of fruit eaten, there was little quantitative information on the types of vegetable food taken by Fieldfares until the marvellously methodical work of Barbara and David Snow during 1980-85. They systematically watched a wide variety of species feeding on fruits in Buckinghamshire and Hertfordshire in southern England, mainly making timed observations, and also noted the way in which the fruit was reached. They found that Fieldfares usually fed gregariously and often in company with other thrushes. Of all the thrushes that the Snows recorded, Fieldfares fed on the smallest number of different fruits: only twelve native species were taken, with just four being really important. The early flocks fed predominantly on haws, with a peak in November. Most of the haw crop was finished by late November or December, and hips (Dog Rose) then became the preferred fruit, especially in February. Finally, before the birds' departure in April or May, Ivy berries may have been an important food. Holly berries were taken mainly in very severe weather. These four fruits (haw, hip, Ivy and Holly) accounted for 96 per cent of the Snows' feeding records. Sloes, eaten mainly in January, made up a further 2 per cent, with the remainder comprising odd records for whitebeam, Crab-Apple, Elder,

This Fieldfare is just swallowing a haw on a snowy day.

Spindle, privet, Buckthorn and Black Bryony. Their results may have been biased by the behaviour of Mistle Thrushes in defending a food supply, since all the large clumps of Mistletoe, and many Hollies, were protected throughout the winter and thus not available to other species except when the territorial defence of the largest thrushes had been overwhelmed.

When they had a choice, Fieldfares strongly preferred haw to Sloe and Buckthorn. They tended to feed in concentrated bouts, gorging themselves for a minute or two before taking a rest. The intervals between feeds ranged from 17 to 26 minutes, with a mean of 21 minutes. The largest meals recorded, 21 Ivy berries, ten Haws and four hips, each amounted to about 6-7 per cent of a Fieldfare's mean body weight.

Fieldfares seem less agile than the other thrushes when feeding on fruit. Nearly all fruit is taken from a perched position, and only 1.2 per cent of the Snows' records were of sallies to pluck a fruit in flight, compared with 7-14 per cent for the other thrushes. Fieldfares were much more likely than other thrushes to perch and flutter, using their wings to maintain balance. Because of the structure of the bushes, some types of fruit are difficult to reach from a perched position, Ivy being particularly so, but even on Ivy the percentage of sallies by Fieldfares was much lower than that by other thrushes. Most attempts to pluck a fruit were successful, with over 80 per cent success rates for haw and Ivy, but birds feeding on hips were significantly less successful (57 per cent). Hips are much bigger than haws or Ivy berries, and are probably more difficult to detach from the bush without the increased leverage from a sallying flight. The extra size of hips, on average three times the weight of a haw and six times heavier than an Ivy berry, presumably makes them worth persevering with.

Apart from the Snows' records, fifty cases of Fieldfares taking fruit at Bookham Common, Surrey, included 76 per cent of haws and 20 per cent Blackthorn. The Venerable P.H.T. Hartley studied all the thrush family in winter in Britain but recorded Fieldfares taking only haw, Holly and Crab-Apple. In another study in Oxfordshire woodland, they were found eating only haw and Sloe, while large numbers of Fieldfares exploit the haws and Yew berries in the famous ancient Yew wood at Kingsley Vale in Sussex. Sloes were the main food for a flock of 350 Fieldfares that unusually spent November and December in Inverness-shire, while a flock of about 150 Fieldfares fed on Sea-buckthorn fruit in Anglesey in hard weather in 1962, but many became weak and died.

In Continental Europe, Fieldfares stripped the fruit of Guelder-rose in German hedges prior to their autumn migration. In subalpine birch and montane areas of Norway, Juniper and Cowberry were important springtime fruits, having lain over winter beneath the snow, while in autumn Bilberry and Crowberry were favoured. The Rowan appears to be overwhelmingly important in Scandinavia, the depletion of this crop triggering the birds' migration. Heikki Tyrväinen showed that Fieldfares stayed later than normal in Finland in years with plentiful Rowan fruit, even into the depths of winter, and delayed moving out until there were just a few berries left in each clump. However, an exclusive diet of Rowan berries in an Austrian winter led to loss of condition and death. Fieldfare stomach contents analysed from a few birds taken in 17 different areas in

Fieldfares can perch on quite thin branches to reach clumps of berries in Rowan, Elder, Hawthorn and similar fruit.

Hungary showed that the birds were apparently living exclusively on fruits and seeds, of a variety of nine species, for three months from the beginning of December. Johannes Dieberger noted that, following a heavy snowfall near Vienna on 18 December 1981, Fieldfares fed for the next nine weeks almost exclusively on Mistletoe berries, one of the most nutritious of wild fruits. The increase and spread of oak Mistletoe in Austria is said to be due to flocks of wintering thrushes, which excrete the pips of the berries.

The association of birds with Rowan is such that in Germany the tree is called *Vögelbeere*, meaning bird-berry. Feeding on Junipers must have been particularly obvious in Germany for the Fieldfare to be called *Wacholderdrossel*, meaning Juniper thrush. In British winters it has even been suggested that Fieldfares may be responsible for the habit of irruptive flocks of Waxwings feeding in towns, as Fieldfares have stripped the berries in the countryside!

Other than wild species, the only fruits that Snow and Snow saw Fieldfares eat were cultivated *Cotoneaster cornubia*, taken from mid-December to late February. Birds in north Scotland were forced to turn to *Cotoneaster* berries in a prolonged spell of cold weather in 1978/79, when they rapidly lost condition and many died. Elsewhere, a flock of fifteen Fieldfares from January to the beginning of March was recorded feeding exclusively on organic waste from a pig farm after the berry supply was exhausted.

Several unusual feeding habits are on record. Fieldfares have been seen flying high in the air to take flying insects, like Starlings do. One was observed robbing another of its food, but this behaviour (kleptoparasitism) is apparently rare enough to be worth recording. A Fieldfare can use its beak in the style of a Turnstone to turn over clods of earth, and even stones up to 10 cm across, to find invertebrates lurking beneath. In desperate times, they will scratch through snow to reach hidden food, and occasionally they search through leaf litter in the manner of a Blackbird.

Most of the unorthodox methods have been noted in winter, when hard-pressed birds have been seen to enter shallow water to take fish, and also pecking at a dead fish. If they have to, Fieldfares can actually swim, but they have never been recorded swimming to find food. On the Scottish Lothian coast, Bannerman (1954) noted that 'hundreds resorted to the beach at high-water mark, appearing to pick up small marine animals by digging little holes in the rejectamenta of the tide'. During the prolonged spell of cold weather in Britain in December 1981, a dredged land drain in Morayshire provided food for many species, including Fieldfares and Redwings that were seen to swallow small eels up to an estimated 12 cm in length. In the Russian winter, Fieldfares have been known to break ice to pick out fish, water beetles and other aquatic insects. Collinge quoted a report that 'In very hard weather it has been known to do some damage to turnips in its endeavour to ward off starvation.'

At almost all times of year the Fieldfare's diet contains sufficient liquid for it never to need to drink, although individuals are occasionally seen taking water from puddles or streams.

Orchard fruits

Particularly in times of hard winter weather, Fieldfares congregate in apple orchards. This habit has clearly become more prevalent in recent years. For example, David Bannerman, writing in 1954 said that, in hard weather, 'turnips are attacked, and, in rare instances, fallen apples'. Other authors refer to it as if eating apples is unusual and noteworthy, and records such as that of 5000 in a Warwickshire orchard are mentioned time and again in the literature. Since taking a special interest in the species, from the late 1970s onwards, I have found that visiting apple orchards in Cheshire in hard weather is a sure way to find big flocks of Fieldfares, any time from November through to February. They do have their favourite orchards, however, and it is not always obvious why some are regularly frequented while others are only rarely visited. Since at least the 1970s, ringers in several parts of Britain and Ireland have taken advantage of this behaviour to catch large numbers of Fieldfares. As well as my work in Cheshire, I am aware of long-running studies in Herefordshire, Cambridgeshire, and near Dublin in Eire.

My own observations concur with those of workers in several other areas in finding that Fieldfares show a clear preference for certain varieties of apple. The softer, yellower ones are taken first, with Golden Delicious the most favoured, while harder, redder varieties are left until last. I have found no obvious preference for feeding on fruit still on the trees, as opposed to fallen apples, nor for apples at different heights on a tree. Fieldfares in Switzerland, however, fed mainly in the tops of the trees, taking over 90 per cent of their apples from near the crown. They need a good all-round view for their flight into and away from their feeding area, but also need a strong branch to perch on, adjacent to the apple they eat, as they are much less agile in the trees than other species such as Starlings. The differences between my observations and those in Switzerland could be due to the structure of the orchard, with the trees in Cheshire arranged in neat, straight rows, the gaps between the rows affording good visibility, but they could also be a result of the birds in

Cheshire feeding on apples only in hard weather, when they were perhaps forced to be less choosy in their feeding locations.

Their habit of eating fruit in commercial orchards will potentially bring Fieldfares into conflict with man, but the economic effects of Fieldfares on horticulture have been rather little studied. In Switzerland, the damage done to apples by Fieldfares depends on the availability of sufficient earthworms, and also on how late it is before the apples ripen and are harvested. It seems that few apples are lost to local birds, most of those that are taken falling from the end of October onwards to the flocks of northern immigrants. The worst-hit orchard was one at a high altitude, thus ripening late, that had the misfortune to be situated near a thrush roost. Besides the damage to apple-growing, Fieldfares in Norway and Finland have also harmed commercial crops of strawberries, currants and cherries. At the time of cherry ripening, one nest in Switzerland was found with large numbers of cherry stones littered around its rim. Damage has also been reported to pears and to an Italian olive grove.

My main study orchard at Daresbury is managed on a 'Pick-your-own' basis, with customers taking their own apples straight from the trees. Not all are picked by the end of the season (approximately the end of November) and it is not economic for the farm to harvest them, so they are left to be taken by birds, mainly Fieldfares and Starlings. The birds almost invariably clear all remaining apples by February, and are considered by the farm manager to perform a useful role in removing over-ripe or rotting fruit that might otherwise harbour pests or disease. Occasionally I have found birds to be disoriented, apparently intoxicated from the effects of eating over-ripe, fermenting, apples, and twice I have caught 'drunken' birds by hand, both of which flew off strongly after being kept for about 30 minutes in a dark place.

By mid-February at the latest, all the apples will have gone, either eaten, rotted away or cleared by the orchard farmers. Freezing conditions this late in the winter are particularly difficult for Fieldfares, and they resort to any remaining berries, becoming more likely to enter urban areas and gardens, although the lengthening days make survival somewhat easier than in mid-winter frosts.

Defence of a food supply

Individual Fieldfares may defend a food supply, even a single apple in a garden during freezing weather, but this behaviour is much less well developed in this species than in the Mistle Thrush. When guarding a fruit source, the Fieldfare sits prominently on the bush itself or a nearby suitable perch, and adopts a posture - when other thrushes come near - with wings lowered to display their white underwing-coverts: this is a feature shared only with Mistle Thrushes, and it is tempting to think that the flash of white has evolved as a warning sign. Snow and Snow (1988) found eleven individuals, ten of them apparently adult males, defending suitable clumps of fruit against other Fieldfares, and other species, but particularly the thrush family. All but one of their records came from the coldest part of the winter, and their birds defended haws (four records), hips (four records), a mixed clump of haw, hip and Black Bryony, and garden *Cotoneaster cornubia* (two cases). No defence lasted for very long, the maximum recorded being about two weeks, whereas Mistle Thrushes often defend their supplies for months on end. The Snows' quantitative observations showed that feeds tended to be smaller for defended fruits, six on Hawthorns averaging 4 berries, compared with 6.9 on undefended bushes. The mean time between feeds on a defended supply was shorter than on undefended fruit, at 14 minutes (ranging from 7 to 20). Thus, a Fieldfare defending a fruit source tended to take smaller meals but fed more often.

In the orchard at Daresbury where I have spent so much time, there was no evidence of territorial behaviour by feeding Fieldfares, and they fed in flocks that apparently moved *en masse* through the orchard. Alan Tye was able artificially to induce Fieldfares to defend a feeding area, by placing apples in an open field, but eventually this defence proved uneconomical in the face of intrusions by other Fieldfares and Starlings.

It is interesting to consider why Fieldfares only occasionally defend food supplies, while this is a normal way of life for Mistle Thrushes. Fieldfares are more gregarious, and usually stay in an area for only a short time, a few days or weeks at most. Mistle Thrushes probably defend part of their territory all the year round, and may reap the benefits of their behaviour in the following breeding season.

Fieldfares are often at the receiving end of the territorial defence of Mistle Thrushes, which are usually effective at keeping away all other birds. However, Mistle Thrushes defending a tall garden *Cotoneaster* in hard weather in Britain were reported to drive off Fieldfares and Redwings but appeared to tolerate thrushes feeding on fallen berries underneath.

Fieldfares sometimes defend a food supply, adopting a posture with wings lowered to display the white underwing coverts, a feature shared with Mistle Thrushes.

How much food do Fieldfares need to eat?

Before considering how much a Fieldfare has to eat, we must first know how much energy it uses up each day. The subject of avian energetics has attracted a lot of study by professional ornithologists, and it is now fairly well understood how much energy a bird needs to survive, and how much is consumed in each of the daily activities such as standing, running, flying, and so on. The figures for wintering Fieldfares have been worked out by Alan Tye. The absolute minimum mid-winter requirement for a bird weighing 120 g, assuming an idyllic existence with temperatures as high as 10°C and all the time spent gently feeding or roosting, with no energy-intensive flights or fights, is about 220 kJ a day. Desperate conditions, with sub-zero temperatures and scarce food that takes much flying to find and then has to be fought over, will at least double this. So, a Fieldfare needs to take in about 40 kJ of energy every hour of a nine-hour day when the temperature is 3°C. If the temperature falls to -5°C, its intake has to increase by about a quarter. It uses about 130 kJ of energy each night in keeping warm, so each bird must gain on average a net 14.5 kJ per hour during the nine hours of daylight feeding time in order not to have to deplete its long-term reserves in the night.

The amount of energy gained from food depends on its composition, and on how readily it can be metabolized. Birds build up reserves in the form of carbohydrates, proteins and fat. In general, carbohydrates provide about 16-18 kJ of energy per gram of weight, and they are used in activities of short duration, such as the first few minutes of flight. As the flight continues, or as the bird keeps warm overnight, fatty acids become the main fuel, with a high energy yield of 38-40 kJ per gram. Storing fat, usually just below the skin, is the most efficient way for birds to build up reserves. Burning proteins gives the bird about 18-24 kJ per gram, but proteins are important for more than just their energy content, enabling the bird to maintain the right balance of essential amino acids.

Fieldfares flocking in a typical rich pasture can gain energy from feeding on worms at a rate of 2.5-4.2 calories per second (38-64 kJ per hour). The energy content of apples is about 2.5 kJ per gram fresh weight, with a lot of that weight being water, and Fieldfares typically take about 1 g per minute. Thus, assuming a 50 per cent assimilation efficiency, birds feeding on apples can achieve an energy intake of about 75 kJ per hour, and each bird needs to eat about 300 g daily, perhaps two good-sized apples a day. These figures indicate that Fieldfares need to spend roughly half of their time feeding, either on worms or apples, to satisfy their daily energy needs, although in winter they have difficulty obtaining sufficient energy by hunting invertebrates. Alan Tye, who put in a lot of time studying the feeding ecology of Fieldfares in open country in Cambridgeshire, with haws the main wild fruit available, concluded that, when readily accessible, haws can easily provide sufficient energy for the birds' daily needs.

Food has to give more than just energy, however, and there is some dispute about whether feeding on fruit alone can provide all the necessary protein and vitamins. Certainly, the Fieldfare's favourite berries, such as Mistletoe, Sea-buckthorn and Rowan, are quite protein-rich, each having

1.3 – 1.5 per cent of their fresh weight as protein, although apples are only about 0.34 per cent protein. In February 1978, Fieldfares on the North Sea coast of Germany were found dying after eight days of freezing weather despite a sufficient supply of apples. Starlings can digest barley rapidly to put on weight quickly, while invertebrates take longer to find for the equivalent weight gain, but captive birds fed on barley alone cannot maintain their weight, even when consuming more than their own body weight per day.

This was also true in Peter Berthold's experiments on captive Blackbirds, Robins, Blackcaps and Garden Warblers: no bird was able to maintain its weight on an exclusive diet of fruit, and he suggested that this was due to protein deficiency. Given unlimited access to fruit, only small amounts of insect food (just 2 - 3 g for Blackbirds) were needed for the birds to maintain body weight. However, Snow and Snow point out that Berthold's birds were atypical in eating only small weights of fruit (25 per cent of their body weight each day for Blackbirds, as opposed to a typical value for observed wild birds closer to 75-100 per cent), so Berthold's conclusions may not be fully applicable to birds in the field. Also, the measure of a bird's weight alone is a crude indicator of body condition and may conceal other physiological changes such as a change in lipid concentration or water retention.

Thus, it is still debatable whether fruit alone is sufficient for long-term maintenance of body condition. In winter, however, Fieldfares often have little choice, and David and Barbara Snow concluded that 'it seems probable that Fieldfares can survive lengthy periods of severe weather on a diet of fruit, but only if it is of high enough nutritive quality.'

4

VOICE

The voice of birds is undoubtedly their most neglected aspect, by amateur and professional alike. Unfortunately, the present-day emphasis on recording the minutiae of plumage is pushing knowledge of vocalisations even further into the background and leaving generations of birders with little appreciation of the importance of bird sounds. For sure, identifying bird song is not always an easily acquired skill. The best way to learn is by careful observation and listening in the field, although the many good sound recordings now available can also help. It is well worth taking the trouble to study birds' voices, for understanding them can open up different facets of birdlife.

This raises the problem of how to describe bird sounds. The encyclopedic *Birds of the Western Palearctic* (vol. V, page 21) introduces its section on 'Voice' with the sentence: 'Exceptionally complex and difficult problems

A male Fieldfare starting to sing.

are met in attempting to develop a scientific method of describing and interpreting the vocal utterances of birds.' The most precise way of putting sounds on paper is with sonagrams, analyses of the frequency spectrum, but for most people they are as difficult to understand as would be a description of colours by giving their wavelengths. In this chapter, therefore, I have fallen back on representing sounds by the use of phrases such as 'chack-a-chack'. Many sonagrams are given by Lübcke and Furrer, and by others in *Birds of the Western Palearctic*, but, for our purposes, the key point is to link the sound with its meaning to the birds, and not to give an absolutely accurate depiction of the vocalization.

Even its greatest admirer would have to admit that the subject of this book is not one of the avian world's star singers! The Fieldfare's closest relatives are

A male Fieldfare in songflight: they fly around the territory with short, stiff wingbeats.

some of the best, at least to northern Europeans: the Blackbird, Mistle Thrush and Robin, with the Nightingale as a 'second cousin': but the Fieldfare's song is one of the weakest, most disjointed and tuneless of all the passerines.

The song has more of a warbling quality than those of the other members of the thrush family, but lacks the clear fluty sounds that are so characteristic of other British thrushes. Some have likened parts of the Fieldfare's song to the twittering of a Swallow. Fieldfares differ from other thrushes in often giving song in flight over their breeding area. R. Arnhem, when studying the first few birds to breed in Belgium, was surprised to find the male regularly giving a modulated warbling song when, after feeding the young in the nest, it flew off towards the feeding pastures; no song was ever given while perched. Douglas Weir elicited a similar response of songflight after he ringed the young in a nest in Inverness-shire.

Fieldfares have a territorial call, like 'dschrät-schrätt' or 'trätt-trätt', that is given by males to attract a female, or by either sex in defence of territory, thus serving the usual functions of song. They usually string together these disyllabic calls into long series, and may follow them by a melodious, hiccoughing sound described as 'gnüg', which is also interposed into their feeble attempts at singing.

Although its song is nothing special, the subsong of the Fieldfare has a far-carrying and rather special quality, probably in part because - at least for most English observers - it is usually given 'out of season' and makes one think of the far-northern lands to which the birds will soon be returning. I have heard a flock of over 400 in a large wood in Cheshire in early May, their chuckling subsong audible from over 800 m away on the other side of the wood. When disturbed, they flew off with the characteristic noisy cackling, gaining height and flying north-east until lost from sight. A similar mixture of twittering and warbling is sometimes heard as birds gather at their roost in spring. A burst of subsong from one bird will often stimulate others to join in, and Redwings sometimes add to this glorious northern chorus.

Despite its lack of a distinguished song, the Fieldfare is otherwise a rather noisy bird. Its commonest call is usually transcribed as 'chack-chack' or 'chack-a-chack', and these strident notes are often the first indication that an observer will have of a Fieldfare's presence. This call is often given by flocks when manoeuvring to land, or when flushed. There are several variants of this basic call, all obviously recognizable as Fieldfare, including 'cha-cha-cha-chack', but careful listening shows that the raucous call is almost always preceded by a softer note, almost like an intake of breath, making a closer rendition 'ter-chack-chack'. I have not been able to find any evidence for Ray's suggestion, mentioned at the beginning of this book, that the reason for this hoarse chattering note is that the sides of the fissure in the palate are rough. Eric Simms recorded a bird sitting in a tree and uttering the typical call at intervals of about 25 seconds, occasionally

A male giving its chuckling subsong in spring.

injecting a softer 'chuck-chuck' phrase. This desultory kind of calling is not uncommon from perched birds, perhaps particularly when they are slightly uneasy. When I have been out on dark winter mornings, setting mist-nets in a favoured orchard feeding site, long before first light the earliest Fieldfares fly in with a soft 'chook-chook' call, which changes to the harsh 'chack-chack' only when they realize there is an intruder in their midst.

Daytime parties of flying birds keep up a constant flow of 'chack-chack' calls, but it is unusual to hear any calls from Fieldfares flying over at night. This is another way in which they contrast with Redwings, which are generally more vocal at night than by day, their thin 'tseee' call being such a noticeable feature of clear October nights, and occasional March ones as well. Ken Williamson, however, in 1965, described how he had heard Fieldfares calling as they circled the lighthouse on Fair Isle, mesmerized by its beams piercing the night sky. It is interesting that Fieldfares do have a soft drawn-out note not unlike a Redwing's, transcribed as 'huit', and apparently serving as a distant contact call between members of a loose flying flock.

As with most birds, Fieldfares distinguish between aerial and ground-based predators by making different alarm calls. That for flying predators is a pure high-pitched tone, difficult for humans to locate, and similar to that given by other thrushes. They warn each other of the approach of terrestrial predators by giving a deep, rather muffled, single call, rendered 'quok' or 'tock'. I have often heard a churring call from squabbling winter feeding birds, similar to, but clearly distinguishable from, the usual call of the Mistle Thrush. They frequently give bill-snapping sounds in similar circumstances. Interestingly, David and Barbara Snow mention that Fieldfares adopt the 'Mistle Thrush' type of call when chasing off other birds from a defended fruit supply. This is probably similar to the rattling call heard when man approaches a breeding colony, given by the lookout birds as a warning to the sitting females or their young. If more intense nest-defence is called for, with birds mobbing and defecating on the intruder, this rattling call becomes more strident, and gives way at the moment of defecation to a loud screech. In other situations when they feel acutely threatened, most notably when handled for ringing, Fieldfares can emit ear-piercing screams.

The young Fieldfares have rather different calls. The food call of nestlings is a thin chirp, like that of a House Sparrow. After fledging, food calls and contact calls with parents seem to vary quite a lot, including those rendered as 'zrii-zri', 'pssie' and 'qui-quick'. When being fed, the young often give noisier sounds, like 'trat-zri-zri', apparently starting to develop towards the adults' 'chack-chack', although the fledged young give a more muffled version of that familiar call.

5

BREEDING

Fieldfares are very scarce summer birds in Britain, and rather little has been written about their breeding here. They are on the Special List of Schedule 1 under the U.K. Wildlife and Countryside Act 1981, and must not be disturbed without a licence. They are, however, plentiful through much of Continental Europe, where their breeding habits have long attracted interest, and this chapter is based entirely on the published literature, particularly from Germany and the Scandinavian countries.

Breeding habitat

The Fieldfare inhabits three climatic zones, the subarctic tundra, the boreal and the temperate. It breeds in the middle and higher latitudes, in woods of birch, pine, spruce, alder, and mixed species, usually in open growth or on the fringes of moist areas with grass cover. It is often found along rivers or in groups of trees in fens or bogs, in sheltered but cool and humid situations. As befits a northern bird, it does not tolerate too much heat, but neither does it breed in the coldest regions and its breeding range is rather closely described by the area having a mean July temperature between 10°C and 20°C.

In Scandinavia, breeding Fieldfares are found in habitats as diverse and as far apart as the city parks and gardens of Stockholm and the willow and birch scrub of the low alpine zone above the tree-limit in Lapland, even above 1000 m where Juniper and Dwarf Birch afford sufficient shelter. Between these extremes, they also nest in birch, alder and mixed woods of valleys and hillsides, and in lowland farming country. They will also nest on rocky outcrops in the folds of exposed fells, or on stony slopes with a few straggling bushes, recalling the habitat of their close relative the Ring Ouzel. They have even been recorded breeding on the open tundra beyond the tree-line; this resembles the habit of another relative, the American Robin, the Nearctic replacement in the niche occupied in Europe by the Blackbird. Also like the adaptable American Robin, Fieldfares have taken to nesting in towns, parks, orchards, gardens and even tree-lined streets. In Britain, they have nested in a wide range of habitats: scrub in moorland valleys, wooded hill slopes, farmland, forestry plantations and wood edges.

Fieldfares nest from sea level to well above the tree-line. In Switzerland they are recorded commonly to 1300–1500 m above sea level, but not often above 1700 m, extremes including nests on alpine chalets at 2090 m a.s.l. in Bern canton, at 2070 m near Zermatt and at 2150 m in the Anniviers valley in Valais canton. More recent records have stretched to 2200 m near Zermatt and 2400 m in Graubünden in south-east Switzerland, where there are neither trees nor bushes and the birds apparently nested on the ground: this is the highest recorded nesting that I have been able to trace. Elsewhere in the Alps, in Austria, there are recent records at 2180 m and 2310 m. In Scandinavia, Fieldfares nest from sea level to well over 1200 m. They have recently spread to breed at 1500 m in Kazakhstan, a colony of about 40 pairs exists at 1650 m in Bolzano (Italy), and the normal range in Bavaria extends to 1600 m.

Courtship and pairing

Towards the end of the winter, the males have worn away most of the grey tips to their head feathers, becoming almost black-headed, and some of them start to become quite aggressive, particularly on bright spring days. Territorial disputes have been recorded in the flocks on passage, and intensify after the arrival on the breeding grounds. At the start of the breeding season, males are particularly combative. They choose potential nesting areas and fly at their rivals with sporadic 'chack' calls. Later on, the male calls almost non-stop while performing a threat display with a horizontal posture, his plumage ruffled out, and flicking and shaking his fanned tail while he lowers and twitches his wings. This type of display has the effect of showing the maximum amount of black, in the breast feathers and the uppertail. He also takes up high perches and silently chases his rivals well beyond the territory boundaries. Resident males attack infringing rivals from behind, but if the other bird turns around both will flutter upwards in a tussle, like Starlings squabbling over food, and sometimes fall to the ground interlocked. Birds in disputes sometimes snap bills. The territorial disputes usually become more intense during the pre-laying period until the boundaries are settled, but the males remain aggressive until after the young fledge.

Males often sing in flight, particularly at the beginning of the breeding season, mostly in the early morning and evening. The songflight differs distinctively from the normal undulating flight, the male flying horizontally with slow, deliberate, wingbeats interspersed with the wings being held out stiffly, not quite fully extended. Songflight appears to be performed in a variety of circumstances, all related to a general level of excitement, including when flying to and from a roost, entering or leaving the territory, accompanying the female during nest-building and after confrontations with predators. Its function is thus considered unlikely to be the same as that of the normal territorial song of other passerines, for which Fieldfares use the 'dschrät-schrätt' or 'trätt-trätt' call. The lack of a far-carrying song is presumably ascribable to the Fieldfare's semi-colonial habits: defending only a relatively small area around its nest site, it has little need to sing strongly to keep other males at bay, leaving attraction of a female as the only role for its territorial calls.

When the females arrive, the 'chack' calls are replaced by territorial calls. Their courtship is apparently quick and has been little observed, even by workers studying the species. If a female lands near a male, he falls silent and performs a threat display. If she responds similarly, he will drive her off; if she remains passive, the male will approach her and give an advertising display which is almost the opposite of the threat display, with

The male's threat display shows the maximum amount of black, in the breast feathers and the upper tail, in an attempt to drive off other males.

tail and head dropped, wings stiffly held and drooping away from the body exposing the white underwing coverts and minimising the amount of black shown. This display may be on the ground but is most often given in a tree: the male hops slowly through branches, moving around the female in ever-decreasing circles. During the display, he usually gives a quiet courtship song of muffled chattering sounds with his bill closed. Occasionally, a quivering display flight has been seen.

There is no ceremony before copulation, the initiative coming from either partner. They usually mate in their nest tree or a nearby lookout tree, often within a metre of the prospective nest site. Copulation is most frequent from three days before the first egg to three days before the last.

Apparently, Fieldfares are always monogamous. It is not obvious to an observer how they establish and maintain the pair-bond, given their quick

The male's advertising display to a potential mate is almost the opposite of the threat display, with a submissive posture, minimising the amount of black shown.

pairing, and little courtship or song or any form of territorial display. Normally, the pair stays together for one season; breeding by the same pair in successive years is exceptional. During the breeding season, birds that have lost a mate have been known to find another within four or five days.

Even where they nest close together in colonies, there are only two possible cases on record of females laying eggs in a nest that is not their own. This behaviour is known as egg-dumping or intraspecific brood parasitism. However, this is not always easy to detect from the appearance or timing of the eggs, and application of the technique of DNA finger-printing to Fieldfares may shed new light on intraspecific behaviour. Without such microbiological study, it is almost impossible to spot the other example of 'unfaithful' breeding biology – males copulating with females other than their own mate ('extra-pair copulation').

There are however, a few known instances of hybridization between different thrushes. A male Fieldfare has been known to breed with a female Blackbird, producing four hybrids that looked like Fieldfare chicks. At least two mixed pairings with Redwings have also been recorded in Scandinavia.

Timing of breeding

The Fieldfare is the latest of the thrushes in its normal breeding season, but there are large differences dependent on latitude and altitude, with a range of at least two months from the earliest to the latest. Most of the more obvious variations follow the general bioclimatic laws, whereby spring arrives about four or five days later for each 1° increase in latitude, and about four or five days later for each 125 m rise in altitude. Spring also tends to be later the farther one moves from the sea towards the centre of a continent, but this effect can be much modified by local winds and micro-climate. In general, Fieldfares time their breeding to coincide with the onset of spring weather, but, as with most facets of biology, there are natural-selection factors pushing in different directions. In many areas, the earliest breeders are penalised by reduced nestling survival owing to starvation, although farther north the season is so short that the pressure is to breed as soon as there is sufficient ground clear of snow to allow good feeding. On the other hand, late-breeding Fieldfares risk their own survival by not having sufficient time with good food supplies to complete the moult before the approaching winter forces their migration.

Males typically return to breeding areas a week before the females although some Fieldfares establish pair-bonds during the spring migration, with territorial disputes and nest-site searching observed among passage flocks. For the well-studied population breeding at Hessen in Germany, in years of mild weather the first males arrive in February, while in other years there may be none until the end of March, when males and females arrive together, already paired. First-year birds arrive later on the breeding grounds, but there is apparently no information on the normal age of first breeding. Most passerines of the size of Fieldfares and smaller breed at one year of age, although with Starlings there is a marked sexual difference: one-year-old females attempt to breed but most males wait until they are two years old. It would also be interesting to know (but apparently has not been studied) whether adults prefer to mate with other adults rather than with first-years, and whether breeding success differs with age.

On the west coast of Norway, at about 60°N, Fieldfares usually arrive in the second week of April (Håland 1984). About a week later they are seen in the inner fjord districts. In the subalpine birch zone, at 600–900 m, they arrive around 10 May, and higher up, in the alpine region at 1250 m, around 20 May. The pre-laying period on the breeding ground lasts about two to three weeks, during which they select nest sites and build their bulky nests. Frequent chases take place, both near nest sites and over the heaths where the birds feed, but it is not known whether this is sexual or territorial behaviour.

In the coastal lowlands of Norway, egg-laying is around the beginning of May. The small population resident near Julianehåb in southern Greenland at about the same latitude (c. 60°N) lays around the middle of May. In northern Siberia, at similar latitudes but without the warming influence of the sea, first-egg dates are usually in the first week of June. In the rich subalpine birch forest, 500 – 600 m at Ammarnäs, in north Sweden, the start of egg-laying varied among years from 17 to 31 May depending on weather conditions; the first eggs each year were laid just one or two days after the snow cover thawed. The peak time for first eggs in the highest-lying Norwegian uplands was around 10 June: this is among the latest recorded, and is two months later than in Germany. The timing in upland Norway means that hatching coincides with the main emergence of cranefly species, their normally favoured earthworms being scarce in alpine heaths.

It is well established that the timing of breeding in northern climes is linked to snow thawing, but even in milder areas there may be substantial differences in timing between different years, and it is not wise to combine data from different sites in different years. For instance, in the well-studied expanding Belgian population, many Fieldfares breeding in colonies usually start laying in mid-April, although most solitary pairs probably breed later. In spring 1984, prolonged bad weather delayed their arrival, birds returning to breeding areas only from mid-April onwards, several weeks later than usual.

Nest site

The nesting area chosen is generally in the vicinity of suitable foraging grounds, especially humid meadows and pastureland. As with the Redwing, nest sites are often close to water or marshes. There are several reasons why this might be so: in the frozen regions, areas near to flowing water will thaw earliest, and perhaps damp areas provide more reliable food; also, Fieldfares need mud to line their nests, and this will always be available in such damp sites.

Selection of the nest site may take anything from a few hours to several weeks. The male takes the initiative, but his mate makes the final choice. He first leads her to various sites, giving the territorial call to attract her. She then takes over and tests the site by rotating a couple of times, and plucking and tossing aside any obstructing foliage. Nest material may be brought to several sites before one is finally chosen. Sites from previous seasons may be reused, with the new nest being built on top of the old one or the old nest refurbished; of 203 nests in a German study, 28 were used for more than one season, although there is no evidence that the same birds were involved.

In general, Fieldfares nest high, although they will take up almost any suitable site. Exceptionally, nests are built on the ground, but most are in trees, up to 25 m above the ground, according with the comment of Linnaeus, in his *Fauna Svecica*, that the Fieldfare '*maximis in arboribus nidificat*' : it nests in the largest trees. Most nests are above 2 m, but there is apparently no particular preferred height, the main factor determining this seeming to be just the height of trees and the suitable crotch or solid branch that Fieldfares select to support their massive nest.

In this they differ from the other European thrush species, which tend to have a preferred nesting height, and none of which extends to the great heights shown by Fieldfares. Nests within a colony tend, however, to be placed at similar heights and in the same (or a similar) species of tree. One Norwegian study showed that large females (with long wing lengths) nested higher than small ones, and that heavier eggs were laid at greater heights (Otto 1979). These findings suggest that the fittest birds tend, where they have a choice, to nest at greater heights.

Various studies have shown that Fieldfares tend to build at greater heights in central and eastern Europe, with mean heights of 7 – 10 m, than they do in Russia or Scandinavia, where the mean is 4 – 5 m. This may be due to a lack of taller trees farther north, but is more likely to do with the higher human population density in the former areas.

The species exhibits catholic tastes in its choice of tree species, with nests recorded in a very wide variety of conifers (Silver Fir, larch, spruce, and pine species) and deciduous trees (Sycamore, Horse Chestnut, alder, birch, Hornbeam, Ash, apple, plum, Pear, White Poplar, Black Poplar, Aspen, cherry, oak, False Acacia, willow, lime, and Elder).

Fieldfares exhibit much less variation in their choice of actual nest site, probably because their nest is so bulky that there are only a few places that will support it. About half are in a two- or many-pronged crotch of a thick trunk or against the trunk where a thick branch grows out. The next most popular site, accounting for about a quarter of nests, is on a side branch, distant from the trunk. Most other sites are next to the trunk, supported by thin shoots or twigs. Odd sites on record include one in a shallow tree hole, another on a tree trunk supported by a large tinder-fungus, and others on small boards nailed to tree trunks, suggesting that provision of such artificial 'Fieldfare nestboxes' may help the species to nest in areas of good habitat but without suitable natural nesting trees. In the suburbs of Norwegian seaports, Fieldfares nest freely on trays fixed in the branches for their benefit.

Artificial sites have perhaps been most utilized in areas with few trees, such as in Karelia where the beams of abandoned houses have been used, as have the spans of bridges in Lapland and the doorframe of a wooden hut in Hardangervidda, Norway; above the tree-line in the Alps, nests are often placed on ski chalets. In the Unstrut valley west of Leipzig, where many alternative sites were available in trees, several nests have nevertheless been built on a steel railway bridge, and in Russia nests have been found supported by fences. In Switzerland and Belgium they have been built on rural buildings, and in Belgium on electricity pylons.

Scottish nests have been recorded on the ground, in grass tussocks and heather on the banks of a ditch or stream as well as up to 8 m above the ground in Elder, oak, Sycamore and conifers. Ground nests have also been reported from the Ural mountains, the Siberian tundra, Greenland, and in fissures in rocks in Norway. As well as their vulnerability to a wider range of predators, such nests may be in danger of flooding, especially from melting snowdrifts. In the highlands of Norway, over fifty nests in one colony were placed on the ledges of an almost perpendicular cliff face.

The nest

The nest is built in four or five days by the female Fieldfare, with her mate in attendance. It is cup-shaped, not unlike that of the Blackbird, but is usually much bulkier and untidy. The outer wall is made chiefly of dry coarse grasses, with their long blades arranged horizontally; there may also be small numbers of sticks, stalks and rhizomes of couch grass, the latter being used almost entirely in some sites. Moss is found in the outer portion of about half of the nests examined and about a quarter have lichens and dead leaves built in. On the inside of the nest, the material is cemented with a thick layer of mud, often extending right to the upper edge so that it is visible from outside the nest. The bottom and sides of the nest are lined with a thick pad, usually made of dry and fine blades of grass, but sometimes including fine rootlets, horse hair, fragments of fur, and so on. Artificial materials, paper, string and thread, are sometimes used in nests near houses.

The external shape of the Fieldfare's nest is very variable and conditioned mainly by its site. Nests squeezed in between prongs of a trunk

Unusual nest sites include bridge beams and ledges on rural buildings.

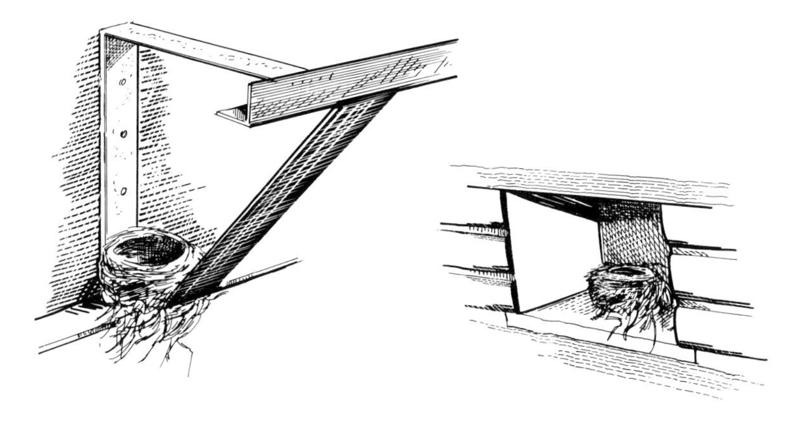

crotch, for example, tend to be narrow and quite tall, whereas those built on a side branch are much broader than they are high. The external dimensions of the nest thus vary greatly, with the outer diameter ranging from 125 to 250 mm and the height from 80 to 200 mm. Despite the extremes of the outer structure, the inside of the nest tends to be elliptical, oval or circular, with a diameter of 80–145 mm, with a mean value of about 100 mm. The internal depth of the nests examined in Latvia varied from 55 to 85 mm, and in Poland ranged from 45–85 mm, with a mean of 67 mm, while those in the northern Urals measured 75–130 mm, averaging 93 mm. Russian ornithologists have considered this difference to be characteristic, with northern nests much deeper than southern nests, and presumably offering better insulation for the nest contents in the colder northern climes.

Eggs

The eggs, laid at daily intervals, are similar in coloration and size to a Blackbird's. They are pale blue, with their red-brown markings very variable, often very heavily speckled, less often blotchy and sometimes forming a cap at the broad end. In shape they are subelliptical, with a mean size of 28.8 mm long and 20.9 mm broad, and extremes of 25.5–35.5 x 17.5–23.7 mm. The last egg to be laid frequently differs in colour from the rest, and is often smaller.

Clutches from northern Europe tend to be slightly larger, but there is no strong increase towards the north, contrary to the results for many other passerine species. The most common clutch size in Fennoscandia and Poland is six eggs, while in Germany and Switzerland clutches of five are the commonest.

As with many species, there is a clear variation in clutch size with altitude. Work in northern Norway, at 60–61°N, found that the number of

A typically untidy Fieldfare nest in the fork of a tree.

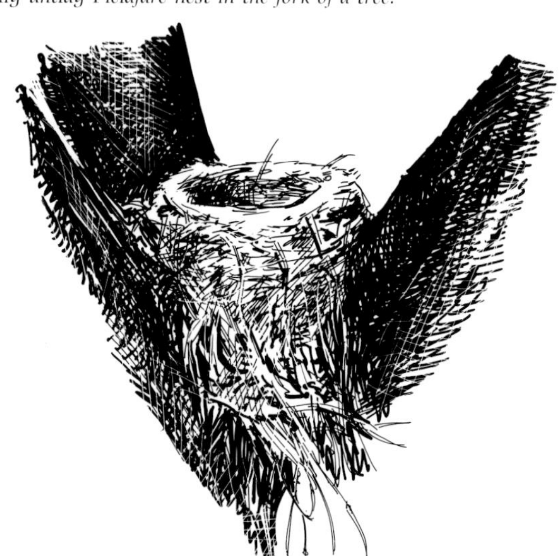

eggs laid decreased strongly from a mean of 5.7 within 200 m of sea level to 5.4 at 600 m above sea level, and only 4.7 at an altitude of 1200 m.

The clutch size also varies through the breeding season. Near Trondheim in Norway, the mean was 5.5 eggs for clutches started up to 20 May, but declined steeply to a mean of only 4.7 in early June (Slagsvold and Sæther 1979). A decline in clutch size is typical of a single-brooded species with a short breeding season. On the other hand, the clutch size of multiple-brooded species with a long breeding season tends to peak in the middle of the season. In a nine-year study in Halle, Germany clutches of five and six were most numerous in April, while the only seven-egg clutches (six nests) were laid in June and July. An increase in clutch size during the season is also found for Fieldfares nesting around Gothenburg in south-west Sweden, where second broods, following a successful first brood, are not infrequent.

In studies in both northern and south-west Sweden, heavier females laid more eggs. The female's weight was not related to her general size, at least as shown by wing length, and heavier females are probably just better fed and more capable of producing bigger clutches. In several species, clutch size is related to the age of the adult, with older birds laying more eggs. If foraging skill increases with age, older parents may be more capable of having larger clutches and producing more fledged young. The relationship between the age of parents and production of young has apparently not, however, been studied for Fieldfares.

The weight of the egg tends to vary depending on the clutch size, with a Norwegian study finding mean values of 5.63 g in four-egg clutches, 6.53 g in five-egg clutches, 6.37 g in clutches of six eggs and 5.96 g in seven-egg clutches (Otto 1979). The weight of the clutch amounts to roughly one-third of the weight of the female. The dry weight of the shell averages 0.36 g, with a range of 0.28 – 0.47 g, and each day during the laying period the hen has to produce this much mineral, mainly calcium.

Incubation to hatching

Only the hen incubates the eggs, for a period of 12 – 15 days with an average of 12.8. Females usually sit tightly, and sometimes allow themselves to be touched while on the nest. The male regularly visits her on the nest, but apparently only rarely actually feeds his mate. The daily cycle of brooding and feeding was studied for one female in Germany throughout the fifth and seventh days of incubation. In addition to sitting all night, she brooded the eggs for almost 90 per cent of the daylight hours, making 16 and 18 feeding forays on the two days, of three to eleven minutes duration.

Incubation often starts from the third egg. Typically three eggs hatch within hours of each other, with the other two or three eggs needing up to another two or three days of incubation. The mean length of the hatching period, from the first to the last chick to emerge, is around 1.8 days for clutches of five eggs and 2.2 days for those of six (Slagsvold 1982). The hatching spread increases for clutches laid later in the season. For nests that escape predation, around 90 per cent of eggs hatch on average: most of the remaining 10 per cent are addled.

Figure 5.1 *Clutch sizes from combining studies in Germany, Norway and Sweden.*

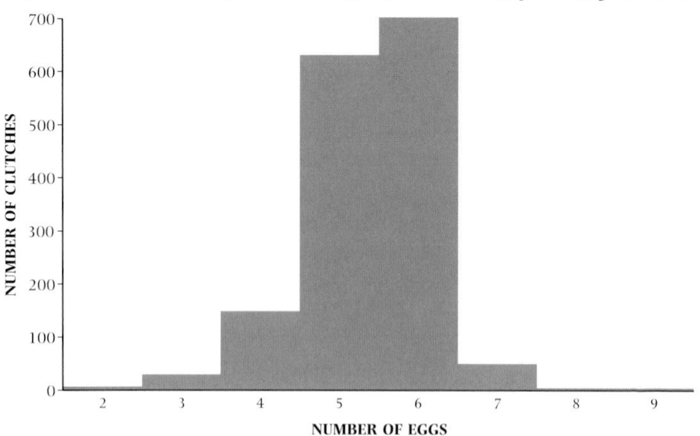

Re-laying after loss of eggs or young is said to be infrequent in the northern populations, but in 1975 a heavy snowfall in northern Norway in late May forced most of the Fieldfares to abandon their nests and many of them re-laid in June. There is an interesting suggestion that some of the Norwegian birds may lay second, or replacement, clutches in a different locality from their first attempt (Slagsvold and Sæther 1979), and German pairs are reported as moving up to 3.5 km after losing a first clutch. It is known that some double-brooded finches do move territories: Linnets prefer to nest in gorse early in the season, the proportion using deciduous shrubs going up for later clutches, while Goldfinches also tend to nest first in conifers in woodland but later move into gardens and orchards; more distant movements may be undertaken by Redpolls, which disappear after breeding in central Europe and arrive at about the same time to start breeding in northern Scandinavia, sometimes accompanied by young birds. Such movement between breeding areas would be impossible to observe without an intensive study of individually marked adult Fieldfares, but an extreme example of such behaviour has recently been proven for another species, colour-ringed Dotterels raising one brood in the Scottish Cairngorms and moving to Norway for a second brood.

There are no reliable reports of Cuckoos laying in Fieldfare nests. In Norway, Cuckoos parasitize about 6 per cent of the nests each of Meadow Pipits, Reed Buntings and Lapland Buntings, while the nests of other, equally common birds, including Fieldfares, Redwings, Song Thrushes and Bramblings are never used. The reasons for this avoidance were explored in some manipulative experiments in which artificial Cuckoo eggs were added to the nests of Fieldfares and Bramblings. Seventeen out of 20 Fieldfares accepted the extra egg, with just one pair abandoning the nest and two others ejecting the Cuckoo egg. On the other hand, the extra egg was tolerated in only two out of eleven Brambling nests: the Cuckoo egg was ejected from one nest, and in three nests, some eggs were destroyed by the adult Bramblings (one bird even managed to make a hole in the thick-shelled hard plastic 'Cuckoo egg'); and five of the Brambling nests were abandoned. For half of the Fieldfares studied, a stuffed dummy Cuckoo was placed near the nest for fifteen minutes with a tape recording of Cuckoo calls being played while the extra egg was added to the nest. A pair of Hooded Crows and a pair of Merlins that nested in the Fieldfare colony received the customary aggressive responses, as did the human observers on every nest visit, but no aggression was shown to the dummy Cuckoo. Adult Cuckoos in Germany, however, were threatened and chased by Fieldfares, which suggests local differences in behaviour.

These experiments show that most Bramblings easily recognize Cuckoo eggs and are unlikely to raise a young Cuckoo. The Norwegian Fieldfares, on the other hand, apparently do not see adult Cuckoos as a threat, and most of them do not recognize a Cuckoo's egg in their own nests. Why, then, are they never used as fosterers by Cuckoos? They may be poor hosts, in which case natural selection will lead to their rejection as potential hosts. Several possible evolutionary explanations may hold good. It may simply be that Cuckoo chicks cannot easily digest the types of food offered by Fieldfares to their chicks and would starve to death, although Cuckoos are known to have been successfully reared by Blackbirds, which bring similar food. Perhaps it is vital for the newly hatched Cuckoos to eject the Fieldfare eggs, as they usually do with host eggs, but they cannot do so because the Fieldfare's nest is too deep or the eggs too heavy. If host specificity is passed to the young Cuckoo either genetically or by imprinting, occasional host species, such as the Fieldfare would be patasitized only by accident. The possibility of genetic transmission in Cuckoos is now being investigated by analysis of mitochondrial DNA, the part of the genetic material that is passed from mother to chicks.

Fieldfare nests are lined with mud. The commonest clutch is of six eggs, pale blue with variable red-brown markings.

OPPOSITE *Typical plumages of Fieldfares (from top) adult male, adult female, first-year and juvenile.*
ABOVE *A female Fieldfare incubating her clutch in a nest in a birch tree.*

Chicks

The chicks hatch naked and blind. Their gape-flanges are yellowish-white and the inside of the mouth is yellow, without the tongue-spots characteristic of many passerine nestlings. They weigh slightly less than 10 g but put on weight rapidly, reaching about 55 g within a week. In this time they grow long, buff-coloured down, around the eyes, on the back of the head, along the spine, on the body covering the roots of the wings and on the trailing edge of the wings: all the parts that are most exposed when the chicks lie in the nest. Their eyes open at about the fifth day.

Young chicks cannot regulate their own body temperature, and have to be brooded to keep them warm, or sheltered to keep the sun off on hot days. They are brooded, by the female only, until they are about eight days old, and usually all night until eleven or twelve days old, when they have grown to fill the nest and the female spends the night roosting on the edge of the nest. For Fieldfares studied in Uppsala, Sweden, the mean length of daylight brooding periods was 30–40 minutes for two-day-olds and 10–25 minutes for eight-day-olds, with substantial variations among the different females studied.

After the first week the chicks' growth then slows with a more gradual rise to about 65 g by the tenth day, as the feathers emerge. The young then become increasingly active, exercising their wings and giving their food-begging call. Many chicks lose weight in the last three or four days they are in the nest, with most of the energy going into growing feathers. Close to fledging, the nestlings are restless and often clamber onto branches around the nest, returning to roost at night. If disturbed when older than nine days, they very often leave the nest prematurely, such 'explosion' being of evolutionary benefit in ensuring that at least some of the brood are likely to escape the predator. They give loud distress calls to attract their parents' attention. Most chicks leave naturally by the fourteenth day, when they beg loudly from the edge of the nest, but some may stay up to three days later than their siblings. Sometimes, recently fledged young adopt a Bittern-like posture, stock-still with their bills pointed vertically upwards.

In Sweden, earthworms are the most important food for nestlings, with other common prey collected for them being craneflies and stoneflies, and, in Lapland, larvae of *Oporinia* moths. The food of the young aged five days and older studied in southern Norway by Meidell (1936) comprised mainly adult beetles (42 per cent of their invertebrate food items), with Lepidoptera larvae (21 per cent) and earthworms (18 per cent); ants (8 per cent) and dipteran flies (6 per cent) were the only other significant invertebrate items. The young had also been given some vegetable matter, mainly the soft, juicy tops of grass leaves and plant fragments (perhaps collected incidentally with the invertebrates from meadowlands, or maybe given deliberately

Figure 5.2 *Typical growth curves of wing length and weight of Fieldfare chicks. In the wild, chicks leave the nest at 12 – 14 days and are independent of their parents at about five weeks. The figures for birds older than ten days are from captive-reared broods.*

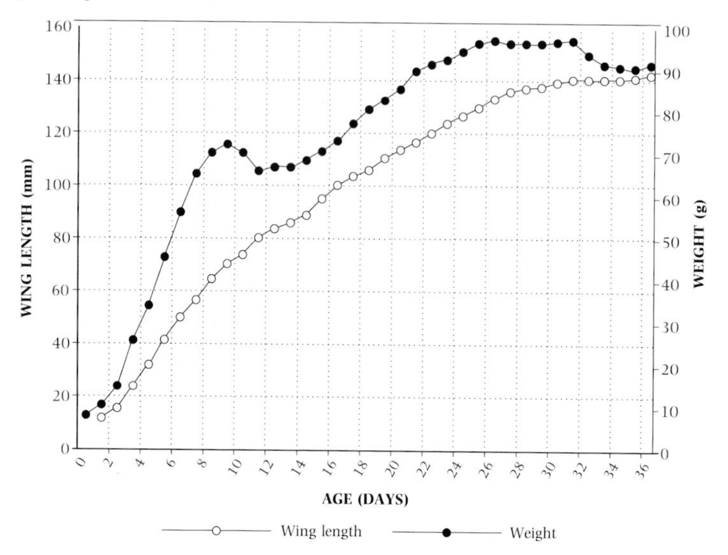

Fieldfare chicks at the ages of two, five, eight, ten and twelve days. By twelve days of age they are recognizable as Fieldfares and almost ready to leave the nest.

as roughage or as a source of minerals or vitamins), and a few berries and seeds. On the other hand, the stomachs of 24 chicks taken from nests in birch or spruce plantations adjacent to pastureland near Bergen, also in southern Norway, contained 64 per cent (by weight) earthworms, 1 per cent Lepidoptera larvae, 7 per cent dipteran flies (larvae and adults), 27 per cent brown vegetation and only 1 per cent fresh vegetation.

Chicks in Germany were fed overwhelmingly on earthworms (52 per cent of their invertebrate diet), with 19 per cent adult beetles, 9 per cent dipteran flies, 4 per cent sawflies, some snails and slugs and the rest being larvae; twelve out of 38 samples contained nothing but earthworms. The proportion of worms and insect larvae in the food given to the German chicks was found to depend on the weather in the preceding two days, with rainy weather increasing their total, although ground temperatures above 3°C are essential for earthworms to be found. In the middle of the day Fieldfares searched for food on the edges of streams, in line with the daily cycle of earthworms where the heat of the day makes them go deeper underground in the pastures. Meidell commented that his chicks were from nests in the Norwegian hillsides and mountains, where earthworms are not particularly numerous, and the butterfly larvae may be thought of as a substitute for the earthworms. He also reported that chicks regurgitate pellets of the hardest and most indigestible matter, which the parents immediately eject from the nest.

Altogether, it seems that worms are more important for Fieldfares than for other thrushes. The different results of these studies may not indicate any consistent difference in food choice between countries, and probably signify no more than the species' catholic diet and tendency to feed on whatever food is locally abundant and anything else they come across while foraging. Most seem to feed near the nest, typically up to 300 m away, but some adults have been recorded carrying food as far as 4 km.

The daily cycle of adults' nest attendance was recorded for one pair in Germany throughout the day when the chicks were seven or eight days old and then five days later. There were 76 and 144 feeding visits respectively, means of 4.5 and 8.5 per hour. Visits to the younger chicks were concentrated into the morning, with 66 per cent before noon and only six visits in four hours in the afternoon, whereas when the chicks were older there were more feeding visits after midday, with 40 visits in the same four hours in the afternoon. Eleven faecal sacs were collected on the first day, with 57 on the second, when the chicks were close to the normal date for leaving the nest.

As with all species that nest well into the Arctic Circle, there is the intriguing question of how the Fieldfares' daily rhythm adjusts to the continuous daylight, but this seems to have been little studied. At one nest in the land of the midnight sun at Neiden, east Finnmark, there was a lull in nest-visiting of about three hours, beginning at 21.00 local time and finishing around midnight, with the most intense feeding activity shortly afterwards.

The foraging behaviour of adult Fieldfares has been studied in Uppsala Botanical Garden, Sweden, where earthworms were always available owing to the periodical watering of the lawns. They were the most common prey taken and were preferentially delivered to the nestlings, while almost all other invertebrate food captured was eaten by the adults. The parents tended to take the largest worms to the young, sometimes eating small ones themselves or eating part of a large one, but usually taking the larger part to the young. Males made three to six feeding visits to the nest per hour; females started at about one per hour with two-day-old chicks, rising to about five per hour when the nestlings reached eight days of age.

An average of 1.5 worms per visit was brought to the nests, with the mean worm length increasing from about 40 mm for two-day-old chicks to 60 mm or more for eight- and twelve-day-old nestlings. A total of 30–60 g of worms per hour was brought to the nests, each chick getting about 10 g per hour. A brood of five chicks in Germany, watched from their hatching date of 29 May to fledging on 11 June, was brought an estimated 3882 g of food, almost exclusively earthworms, an average of 775 g per nestling in two weeks, or about 55 g per chick per day.

As the nestlings in the Uppsala study grew older, males maintained constant feeding rates, delivering fewer but larger worms (and adding up to the same mass per hour). This meant that, when the nestlings were older, fewer of them were fed per visit, but they received bigger meals. Females brood intensively, up to 80 per cent of the time when the chicks are small, and then collect small loads of food in quick spells away from the nest. Later, when they relax their nest attendance, they increase the size of food collected. Thus, the males maintain a constant contribution to brood-feeding during the nestling period, while it is the females that respond to the increasing food needs of the young. Such a marked role separation appears to be unusual in altricial species (those whose nestlings are incapable of locomotion). However, there is an exceptional record in which a female Fieldfare was killed when her chicks were eight days old and the male successfully reared the brood on his own.

Males occasionally pass food to their mates to give to the chicks: the female adopts a begging posture with wing-shivering and gives the thin, high-pitched, Redwing-like call. A female has also been seen to regurgitate water for the young, but their diet normally contains enough fluid for this to be unusual. The brooding female usually swallows the faecal sacs of young chicks in the first week, but later they are carried by both parents. Any chicks that die are removed and carried away from the area.

When an adult returns to the nest with food, this is offered first to the chick with its beak closest to the adult's position. The young are fed from several places on the nest rim, most prey being delivered to chicks positioned close to these places. Late-hatched, smaller nestlings tend to move towards the favoured positions in the nest to counteract selective feeding of the bigger young.

Once, a brood of four under observation died in incessant rain but the female still brooded the dead young. The parents had obviously not learned the 'umbrella' technique adopted by a pair observed on 16 June 1950 in pouring rain in southern Germany. The female was brooding their chicks, which were one to three days old, when the male arrived with food. She appeared to be undecided what to do, presumably not wanting to expose

A resourceful male in Germany acted as an umbrella over his mate and their chicks during heavy rain.

the chicks to the rain, whereupon the male passed the food to his mate and placed himself on the edge of the nest from which the rain was falling, spreading a wing over her as she fed and tended the young.

When a chick first leaves the nest, it can fly only weakly, fluttering to the ground and then climbing up quickly within the tree, the slope of the flutter-flight increasing as it grows older and gains in experience. Young birds stay near the nest, but well dispersed, for about four days until they can fly well, then follow their parents to communal feeding grounds where the juveniles form flocks or crèches. The adults keep on feeding their young for one or two weeks after they leave the nest, the fledglings from late broods staying longer with their parents. As with most birds, adults tend to make their fledged young work for their food, and Fieldfares will approach with a meal in the bill, then hop away, forcing the young to follow. Flightless nestlings from Russian colonies, seeking concealment in thick grass and the underbrush of forests, suffer fairly high mortality from causes including being eaten by dogs and trampled by cattle. Juveniles will beg from strange adults, which usually respond by threat displays, and a female brooding her second clutch may well threaten and peck the chicks from her first brood. After independence, chicks may still beg for food occasionally – once at seven weeks of age – but usually unsuccessfully. There is an extraordinary record of a juvenile Fieldfare that successfully begged food from a pair of adults other than its parents and then went on to brood their young while they were away collecting food; at times, they had to push aside the helper to feed their own young.

If the female starts a second clutch, the male takes over caring for the first brood. At a Fieldfare nest in Scotland, only one egg hatched out of five

A Fieldfare's defecation attack on a Tawny Owl near its nest. Sometimes the predator's plumage becomes so soiled and matted that it cannot fly.

laid in the first clutch, and the pair built a second nest, 30 m away from the first. The female laid the first egg in this second nest only two days after the chick hatched in the first nest; she laid daily and started incubating the second clutch when her first chick was six days old, apparently leaving the male to provide all the needs for the chick in the first nest. This strategy worked well, the chick from the first nest and all five from the second successfully fledging.

Fieldfares suffer extensive predation, with typically half of all nests started being destroyed, but those nests that escape produce large numbers of young. Of 758 nests in the Lake Constance area, 40 per cent produced fledged young, with an average of 4.6 young per successful nest and an overall mean of 1.8 young per nest. Of 159 clutches in West Germany, 52 per cent produced fledged young. In an East German breeding colony studied from 1962 to 1970, the breeding success was very variable: of 198 pairs nesting in the nine years, 105 raised young; out of 798 eggs, 497 hatched, of which 462 produced fledged young, the average annual rate of reproduction being 2.33 chicks fledged per pair. In a study in 1967–75 in central Norway, the average number of chicks fledged per successful nest varied from 3.7 to 5.05.

Defence of the nest

Fieldfares have a spectacular way of protecting their nests against potential predators. They launch themselves in bold dive-bombing attacks, giving rattling calls and often ejecting faeces at the intruder. These attacks have been studied in detail using a stuffed or tethered bird such as a Tawny Owl. The Fieldfare begins its attacking flight aggressively, flying directly with shallow and rapid wingbeats, but brakes and veers off as it comes close to the predator. The rattling call becomes more strident, and gives way at the moment of defecation to a loud screech as the bird turns away. Fieldfares will attack from behind and also defecate on flying predators. Attacks continue until the predator retreats, with the intensity of defecation lessening as the assault continues. The response is fiercest near the nest.

The list of species frequently attacked includes the corvids (Magpie, Jay, Nutcracker, Carrion and Hooded Crows), owls (Tawny, Little and Short-eared), raptors (Goshawk, Sparrowhawk, Buzzard, Black Kite, Red Kite, Kestrel, Hobby, Osprey) and occasionally shrikes, gulls and Great Spotted Woodpecker. The attack behaviour has become increasingly common in the central European population, while it has long been known in Scandinavia.

Possibly, the defecation is a recent addition to the defence behaviour of central European Fieldfares. In Belgium, the smaller predators such as Magpies and Jays are often merely chased, while the full mobbing and defecation is reserved for bigger birds like Carrion Crows and Buzzards.

Typically, one or more birds from a colony fly towards the predator and escort it along the edge of the colony, attacking only if it poses a greater threat. Single crows are attacked only by the birds guarding the colony, but groups of corvids provoke mobbing from the entire colony. Attacks on Hooded Crows are concentrated from behind and on the head, accompanied by much scolding and violent pecking. Fieldfares fly at

Magpies and Jays and ram them from the side. It has been suggested that the lighter grey rump of the Fieldfare may act as a signal in low light conditions, such as inside a forest, and lead the way for fellow attackers, the rump helping to pinpoint the goal of an attack.

Potential predatory mammals such as dogs, cats, Stoats, Foxes and squirrels are usually mobbed. Sometimes humans are attacked, apparently more so in northern countries. This difference is considered to be due to the varying 'flight distance' at which a Fieldfare flees from a predator, resulting from different human population densities on the birds' breeding grounds.

Mobbing often causes the predator to flee, but on occasion an avian victim's plumage may become so soiled and matted that the feathers no longer serve their functions. Several times Buzzards have been encountered that are incapable of flight because their plumage is soiled with Fieldfare faeces. Such defence is apparently necessary, a Buzzard having been recorded taking nine-day-old chicks from a Fieldfares' nest. In 1980 three flightless Buzzards were found in Switzerland and in 1974, in Bavaria, one worker collected 26 Buzzards, five Kestrels and three Sparrowhawks, all of whose feathers were largely stained with excrement.

Mistle Thrushes and Song Thrushes have also been recorded mobbing and defecating on predators, but it is uncommon, whereas it is a well-established and frequent part of the Fieldfare's repertoire.

Colonial or solitary breeding?

Many species of birds breed in colonies, although the habit is uncommon among passerines and rare in the thrush family. There are several factors that may lead birds to breed colonially. Some species, such as seabirds and Sand Martins, have specialized requirements that can be satisfied only at a few sites. For other species that have unpredictable food supplies, a colony may serve as an 'information centre', where those birds that have not fed well can learn from others (this is more frequently suggested as a function of communal roosts). Neither of these reasons applies to the Fieldfare. They nest colonially to protect their nests against predators. The alternative is to space the nests out and behave unobtrusively, but Fieldfares' nests are so bulky that it is not easy to hide them. Clumped prey, however, normally suffers more than randomly distributed prey, even if it is hidden, so normally it would make sense for them to be solitary. The difference for Fieldfares lies in their fierce defence of their nests. They cannot actually prevent potential predators from breeding in the vicinity of their colony, but their nest defence is so persistent that such predators may select areas that are free from Fieldfares in order to avoid the constant harassment.

Colonies vary greatly in their size and structure, with diverse shapes ranging from elongated to circular. The density of nests and the inter-nest distances vary both within and between colonies. Most nests are from 5 to 30 m apart in Scandinavia and Germany, but in Russia there are said to be often four or five nests in the same tree. Depending on the density, the territory occupied by a pair is highly variable: in the centre of a colony, the birds may defend no more than the nest tree itself and their look out perch, whereas solitary breeders may defend areas of up to 1 ha.

The largest colonies are in Scandinavian birch woods, up to hundreds of pairs strong in coastal Norway and covering an area of several hectares. In Sweden, colonies are larger and inter-nest distances are smaller in the north than in the south-west. Solitary pairs are common in southern Sweden but are only occasionally found in the northern woods, where 97 per cent of Fieldfares are in colonies, commonly of 20–30 pairs. On the other hand, colonies are almost unknown in the treeless uplands, as in the barren fell-country of east Finnmark, where the birds breed in widely scattered pairs and the only 'colonies' are of two or three pairs.

The colony size in most situations is limited probably by the availability of invertebrates in the nearby pastures. In rich alder woodland near Trondheim, nine colonies ranged from ten to 55 pairs over six years, with an average of 33 pairs. A subalpine birch forest in central Norway, on the other hand, had an average colony size of 5.2 pairs in a ten-year study. Adults often defend temporary feeding territories, and it has been shown that nestling mortality due to starvation increases with colony size, suggesting that the adults in large colonies put excessive pressure on the adjacent feeding grounds.

Most colonies, however, vary greatly in size, and often change location, from one year to another. One in Germany varied between ten and 45 pairs over nine years. Another in a large countryside park in south-west

A Stoat robbing a Fieldfare's nest in Norway. Two Stoats systematically climbed every tree in the wood searching for food. This one killed the six half-grown nestlings and carried them away one at a time.

Finland suffered total loss of eggs and young in a cold spell in 1968, and the colony was much reduced in 1969, especially at the margins. When a programme of shooting Hooded Crows at a Norwegian site was started in March one year, the number of Fieldfares nesting there in May trebled from the previous year, showing that the Fieldfares on their return from their winter quarters, could apparently detect a 'good' area by its relative absence of nest predators even before they settled to breed.

The benefit of colonial breeding assumes that predators approaching a colony will be mobbed more strongly than near solitary nests. This is indeed so. A study with a Magpie placed near nests with a clutch being incubated showed that, near a colony, the predator was attacked not only by the nearest birds but also by their neighbours. Also, colonial birds attacked more frequently than solitary ones. Usually only the first few attacks are accompanied by ejection of faeces, presumably because they void all their gut contents, but a predator near a colony receives the attention of more birds and thus more attacks than near an isolated nest.

There are conflicting results on whether nest predation is higher or lower in Fieldfare colonies than for solitary pairs. Studies in Sweden and Norway showed that colonies of artificial Fieldfare nests suffer higher predation than solitary artificial nests, and that predation of artificial nests close to breeding Fieldfares is highest near single pairs and lowest in the centre of a colony. They thus found clear benefits to colonial breeders, but no such difference was revealed in northern Germany or in a ten-year study in a birch forest in central Norway.

The mean clutch size in the latter was 5.1 both for solitary and for colonial nests, with 116 solitary pairs and 83 in colonies. From year to year, there was a strong correlation between the numbers of young fledged from solitary and colonial nests, suggesting that both types of nest are subject to similar, but variable predatory pressure. This area seemed to be subject to exceptional predation over the ten years, with 88 per cent of solitary and 83 per cent of colonial nests completely emptied of eggs or small young; in some years, every nest was preyed on, possibly by Pine Martens. At Kazan' in the Volga floodplain, nesting colonies are frequently completely exterminated by Ravens, Magpies and Jays, but the birds re-nest more sparsely and suffer less from their enemies.

The work of Haas (1985), involving 684 broods in southern Germany, demonstrated that early colonial nesters, when the trees are leafless, had significantly higher success than single pairs, but among late broods the nesting success of both categories was the same. There appeared to be some dependence on distance to the next nest, but the colony size, rather than its density, is the most important factor. For early colonies, success increases with colony size, but the opposite applies for the later part of the nesting season. Similarly, a population in the Luzern canton of Switzerland strongly preferred coniferous trees for early nests, but for later nests conifers and deciduous trees became equally common (Furrer 1980).

A very different breeding strategy was adopted in alpine heathland at Langvassmyra in southern Norway. Fieldfares there nested on the ground, spacing their nests 300–1000 m from each other. They behaved in the opposite way to colonial breeders, not mobbing human intruders or using the defecation tactics. Fieldfares when egg-laying tended to leave silently, when incubating were more likely to give alarm calls, and with young always gave the alarm. Only one of the birds ever attacked the observer, when it had young ready to fledge in 1988, and also defecated on him (Håland 1989).

Similar results were obtained by Hogstad, who showed that the level of nest defence towards a potential 'human predator' (the observer) varied from year to year depending on the physical condition of the adults, with fewer and less intense attacks in years when the adults were lighter in weight and carried less fat. It is presumed that the adults' condition reflects the ease or difficulty of finding nutritious food, but one can only speculate about whether the reduced mobbing behaviour is because they have insufficient spare energy, or whether in some way they sense that the feeding conditions will be poor when they need food for their young, and it is not worth their expending much energy on defending nests that are less likely to produce strong fledglings.

The pattern of nest spacing and behaviour observed in alpine heath is likely to be an adaptation to the local predator régime and habitat. Mobbing and defecation are probably very efficient in expelling avian predators, such as crows in woodland, but are probably ineffective against mammals. Foxes can easily reach nests in low trees like the willow bushes used in most alpine habitats, but cannot climb very high, although Stoats can probably climb to all Fieldfare nests. Birds that are badly soiled may not be able to fly, and may die of hypothermia, whereas the big Red Fox will probably be little affected. A parallel exists with Black-headed Gull colonies, where I have often seen that mobbing by the adult gulls repels aerial attacks by crows, but not intrusions by Red Foxes or by Mink. Thus, the type of predator may induce selection for opposite spacing patterns. Mobbing attacks are effective against birds but are less likely to deter mammals. Unfortunately, most workers have not distinguished between the different predator pressures on Fieldfares in different areas.

Coloniality by Fieldfares probably evolved under high predation pressure and the need to breed as early as possible (Haas 1985). Once they had developed their effective anti-predator defence in the form of highly accurate aimed defecation, they could breed earlier and exploit the higher availability of earthworms. Why, then, do many Fieldfares continue to nest singly? There is some evidence that solitary breeding pairs run a lower risk of adult predation, particularly from owls. Predation on adults thus seems to select for solitary breeding. Since neither type of breeding behaviour has died out, there must be a fine balance between the benefits and disadvantages of colonial breeding, probably depending on the variable annual chances of factors such as the potential increased production of young versus the increased risk of predation of adults and the possible total loss of a colony to a predator not deterred by the colonial defence.

One ornithologist has speculated that there might be two distinct Fieldfare populations, the mountain type and the lowland-plains type, but few workers have looked at the behaviour of individual adult birds. It would be very interesting to know whether individuals remain colonial throughout the season, or indeed through their life, or if they adapt to

Newly-fledged birds stay near to the nest for a few days while their parents bring them food.

changing circumstances by shifting between solitary and colonial behaviour. Also, is the same breeding habit adopted by offspring of colonial or solitary adults? The situation is complicated because nobody apparently has studied whether a pair can choose to breed solitarily: if another pair tries to settle nearby, is the latter repelled? If not, the decision whether or not to form a colony is taken by the second pair to arrive, not the first.

It is difficult to summarize the varied results on the success of colonial and solitary breeders, except to point out that it is perhaps obvious that there is no overwhelming benefit of either strategy. If one or the other were patently better, then natural selection would rapidly ensure that the birds that adopted that way of breeding would become much more common. The fact that there are still substantial numbers of colonial and solitary breeders tells us that evolution is maintaining a balance.

Nesting association with raptors and other species

It has long been noted that Fieldfare colonies often tend to contain nests of species that are potentially their predators, particularly falcons and shrikes. Such nesting association is truly symbiotic, for both sides benefit from the increased nest defence against their common enemies, especially corvids and the larger raptors. In one study of the Great Grey Shrike in Ajoie, Switzerland, three-quarters of the 36 nests found were near Fieldfare colonies, and there are many records of nesting associations with Red-backed Shrike, Woodchat Shrike and Lesser Grey Shrike. The main species of falcon found nesting close to Fieldfares are Merlin and Kestrel.

Hogstad (1982), studying Fieldfares breeding in subalpine birch at Budal in central Norway in 1976–81, showed that 33 pairs nesting close to breeding Merlins produced on average 1.73 fledged young per nest, while those 65 pairs of Fieldfare not in association with the Merlins raised only 0.55 young per nest. There was very high predation pressure, probably mainly from Hooded Crows, during the incubation period, and the Merlins were quite effective at keeping such predators at bay. The Fieldfares arrive at the site after the Merlins have started egg-laying, and therefore it is the Fieldfares that choose to be near the raptors, with the colony tending to be centred on the Merlins and the nearest Fieldfare nest always within 30 m of the falcons' nest. In 1981, the Merlins moved to a new site where there had been no Fieldfares in the previous years, but a group of Fieldfares found them and formed a breeding colony around their nest. The six Fieldfare nests around the traditional Merlin nest site that year all failed. The additional protection afforded the Fieldfare colony by the Merlins is clearly very important in any area with high pressure from predators.

Another study, in Sweden, showed that the Merlins also benefit when surrounded by Fieldfares. From 1971–75, 36 Merlin nests were observed in an isolated subalpine birch forest, 29 of which were in Fieldfare colonies. The seven solitary Merlins raised an average of only 1.14 young per nest, while those nesting near Fieldfares averaged 2.95 fledglings per nest.

Some other passerine species also nest in Fieldfare colonies, and in these cases there is apparently benefit to them but none for the Fieldfares, except that there are more small birds around to spot potential predators and give alarm calls. A breeding colony in Germany, in meanders and oxbow lakes of the River Unstrut, also contained nests of Goldfinch, Chaffinch, Greenfinch, Icterine Warbler, Starling and Golden Oriole. Near Trondheim in Norway, most Chaffinches start breeding just before the Fieldfares, and therefore it is mainly luck if their nest happens to be inside an active

Typical Fieldfare breeding habitat: Norwegian birch scrub.

colony, unless somehow they react to the same environmental clues. On the other hand, most Bramblings start breeding after the Fieldfares and can choose to nest within a colony, and a much higher proportion of Bramblings than of Chaffinches do nest in association with Fieldfares (Slagsvold 1979). Where the siting of Fieldfare colonies changed from one year to another, Bramblings tended to move with them.

Both finch species do better within Fieldfare colonies: Chaffinch nests were robbed less frequently than those outside, and Bramblings laid more eggs. In Russia, Chaffinches nest slightly later than in Norway and often choose to nest in Fieldfare colonies, with higher breeding success. In some areas, Redwings apparently choose to nest in such sites, and once three *Turdus* species were found nesting within a 9-m radius, a Song Thrush, a Redwing and two pairs of Fieldfares. Redpolls and Icterine Warblers apparently also seek nest sites within Norwegian Fieldfare colonies, and other species may well do so, including Siskin, Willow Tit, Spotted Flycatcher and Yellowhammer. Three or four cases have been reported of Wood Sandpipers nesting in old Fieldfare nests 3.5 m up in birch trees in Sør-Tröndelag, inland in central Norway. Similarly, Green Sandpipers frequently nest in trees using old nests of other species and have been recorded using Fieldfare nests in Fennoscandia and Poland.

For any of these species, if nesting with Fieldfares is hereditable, or learned by imprinting in the juvenile stage, it is clear that the increased success of birds doing so will exhibit a strong selection pressure and behaviour will rapidly evolve to favour such associations.

On the other hand, some species of small passerine, including Dunnock, Robin, Coal Tit and Bullfinch, seem to nest at lower densities in areas with Fieldfare colonies than in similar habitats without Fieldfares, and perhaps they suffer from increased interspecific competition when there are more birds of other species present. These species are archetypically from the southern lowlands, whereas most of those that increase with Fieldfare density are northern subalpine species, and it seems that the presence of a Fieldfare colony tends to shift the balance of species towards a more northerly pattern. This idea has led Tore Slagsvold to suggest that there could be a 'Fieldfare effect' on the population dynamics and geographical expansion of several other northern species.

Jays, Siberian Jays, Magpies and Hooded Crows tend to avoid breeding in Fieldfare colonies, probably because of the constant mobbing. Woodpigeons also avoid them, possibly because their shape is similar to raptors and evokes aggressive responses from nesting Fieldfares.

In the alpine region in the Arctic Circle rodent plagues occur regularly, usually on a four-year cycle. During peak years, the populations of predators such as Merlins and Hooded Crows also peak. The rodent eruptions apparently can occur at any time of year and may not be synchronized with the birds' breeding cycle. In 1975, the lemming population in northern Sweden reached a peak in May and then crashed within a month. This sudden decrease in prey forced predators to find other food, and nest predation eradicated all 88 Fieldfare clutches under observation by Christer Wiklund. Such a catastrophic plundering occurred only once during a twelve-year study, covering three rodent cycles.

Breeding strategy

In Switzerland most Fieldfares are double-brooded, but elsewhere few of them lay second clutches. These are certainly rare among the northern Fennoscandian Fieldfares, but even in the expanding population near Lake Constance on the Swiss/German border only about 20 per cent of 664 pairs laid second clutches. This contrasts with other thrushes, with Blackbirds, Song Thrushes and Redwings regularly laying a second clutch after successfully rearing one brood. The annual mortality of Fieldfares seems to be higher than that of other thrushes, and this is sustainable only by a high breeding success. This indirectly suggests that the degree of nest predation suffered by Fieldfares is lower than for other thrushes, attributable to their fierce nest defence and colonial habits.

Studies over a wide range of habitats have shown that the most common clutch size for Fieldfares is six eggs. This is also the one producing the most fledged young. Naturally, evolution favours those that produce most young, and there is selection against small broods, but in most species there normally is a balance, with larger broods having relatively higher failure rates and acting as a downward pressure on brood size. For Fieldfares, on the contrary, a study of ringing recoveries from nestlings ringed in Switzerland showed that young birds from nests with up to four chicks tended to survive less well than those from broods of five or six.

Fieldfare broods, on average, are larger than those of any of the other European thrushes, and enable the Fieldfare population to expand rapidly if conditions are favourable. They adopt the strategy known to theoretical biologists as r-selection (from the technical notation for the intrinsic rate of increase of a population). Fieldfares exhibit all of the classic characteristics of such adaptation: they live in unpredictable environments; are fairly small and short-lived; suffer high mortality that is largely independent of their density; have good powers of dispersal; and have a high reproductive rate. However, one can ask why they do not lay even more eggs?

This was tested in experiments involving the manipulation of clutch or brood size by adding eggs or young (Slagsvold 1982). One hundred nests with five or six of their own were increased to seven, and parents that had laid either five or six eggs showed equal skill in raising seven young. They raised seven young more successfully in artificially provided large nests than they did in their own nests, although hatching losses were greater in enlarged nests than in natural nests, and females may have difficulty in incubating seven or more eggs uniformly. Bigger nests probably place the young at more risk of chilling in rain or whenever the female should be brooding them.

The habit of some Fieldfares of hatching eggs asynchronously, relatively unusual in passerines, is normally considered to be a way of maximizing the number of young in an uncertain environment: in periods of food shortage, the smallest young will die, but some young should be reared. Artificially enlarging the brood, however, clearly demonstrated that the Fieldfare normally rears a smaller brood than could be nourished. The reason why broods of seven are not found more commonly may simply be overcrowding of the nest, or it could be the result of a more complicated balance of the

A female feeding one of her hungry brood of six chicks at the nest in a birch in Norway. Their eyes are just open, at an age of five or six days.

energy needed by the female to produce more eggs, or the effort involved from the adults in feeding more young could leave the adults out of condition and weakened so that they stand much less chance of surviving to the next breeding season. However, similar studies with Starlings showed that the key factor in survival of the young was their weight at fledging, and that chicks in artificially enlarged broods left the nest at lower weights than those from more normal brood sizes. Although the Fieldfare chicks from the manipulated broods fledged successfully, it is not known whether they did so at the same weight as those from other broods.

Breeding density

The Fieldfare is not an easy species to census, because of its lack of song and territoriality and habit of nesting either solitarily or in colonies. Nest-finding is probably the best method, but there are problems even with this. Censuses of Fieldfares are hampered by two opposing requirements. The birds' high mobility and the local concentrations resulting from their colonial habit call for covering a large area. On the other hand, the time-consuming need to search for and monitor all nests makes it difficult accurately to cover anything more than a small area. Such a census is then unlikely to be representative of a larger area.

Similar comments apply to figures for breeding density. Some of the very high values that have been quoted, up to tens of pairs per hectare, equivalent to thousands of pairs per km², have been found by covering a small area that includes a colony, or perhaps only the densest part of a colony. On the other hand, a survey of a large region, or even a country, will include many areas that are unsuitable for the species and will thus give a low figure for the average density. The recent population estimate for Sweden (Chapter 2) works out at 3.3 pairs/ km^2 for the whole country, and for Finland at 1.7 pairs/ km^2.

In a widespread study of the breeding birds in urban parks across Finland, the Fieldfare density was found to increase greatly towards the north, with 1.3 pairs/ ha in the mid-boreal range close to the Arctic Circle but with ten to fifty times fewer pairs per hectare in the southern parts of Finland at 60° – 63°N. In a census of breeding birds of farmland across Finland, Fieldfares were among the three commonest species in all regions in the south and east of the country, with a peak density of 17.8 pairs/ km^2 in the east and a mean density over all Finnish farmland of 7.4 pairs/ km^2.

Wolfgang Lübcke studied an area of 17.5 km^2 along the lower river Eder in North Hessen, Germany for five of the years 1967 to 1974; he found an increase in density from 10.7 to 15.9 pairs/ km^2, as the birds increased the colony size and also spread to suboptimal and marginal habitats. A census in the Lippe region of the east Ruhr logged 90–110 pairs in 127 km^2 in one of the most favoured areas, and a total of 500 – 1000 pairs in about 1500 km^2. In an area of 129 km^2 around Karl-Marx-Stadt, near Dresden, 250 pairs were found, almost two pairs/ km^2. In Switzerland, Fieldfares have nested at a density as high as ten to fifteen pairs in 0.5 ha, equivalent to 2000 – 3000 pairs/ km^2, but the mean density in the 370 km^2 of Zurich canton is in the range one to two pairs/km^2.

The published data for Russia are sparse, but suggest a higher breeding density there. The 10-km^2 Gdanov Park in Leningrad held 60–80 pairs of Fieldfares, compared with 30 pairs of Ring Ouzels, ten to twelve pairs of Song Thrushes and three to five pairs of Blackbirds. In a study in the Kemerovo district in eastern Siberia, breeding numbers varied greatly according to the feeding conditions for the returning adults. 1963 was a dry year, with worms deep in the ground, and 272 pairs bred in an area of 14.4 km^2, while 1964 saw a quick snow melt, with many worms near the surface, and there were 379 pairs in the same area, at a density of 26.3 pairs/ km^2.

6

FEATHER MAINTENANCE

It is essential for birds to keep their plumage in good condition, and up to one tenth of the day is spent on the various aspects of feather maintenance, usually called by biologists 'comfort behaviour'. All of the thrushes bathe, lowering the front of the body and dipping the head and breast in the water while splashing with the bill, wings and tail to shower all parts of the body. In Germany, up to 40 Fieldfares have been seen to bathe together at the edge of a gravelly stream, in a flooded area from a leaking tap or in a puddle, with afternoons apparently the preferred time. They dry off by whirring the wings and tail, and restore the feathers' waterproofing properties in the subsequent process of preening, in which the bird takes oil from the preen gland, just above the tail, and spreads it along the feather. For the wing and the tail, each feather is passed through the bill to straighten out the barbs and interlock the barbules. The head is preened by scratching with a foot; the preening oil is usually transferred from bill to foot, and sometimes Fieldfares rub the head against other parts of their plumage. Occasionally Fieldfares have been seen bathing in dust or loose sand, where they make much the same movements and spread the dust in the same way as when bathing in water.

Many birds carry external parasites (ectoparasites), including fleas, chewing lice (*Mallophaga*), ticks, feather lice and *Hippoboscids*, variously known as flat-flies, louse-flies or keds. Some are found on a variety of birds, while others afflict only one species or genus. Sometimes a study of the host-specific parasites can be helpful in deciding the taxonomic relationships between birds, since the parasites may have evolved along with their hosts (Chapter 1).

Mallophaga feed on feathers and blood and often confine themselves to particular parts of the body. At least six species have been recorded on Fieldfares, most of them living only on the breast or on the back. Four of these species appear to be specific to Fieldfares, but two of them are also found on Mistle Thrushes, Song Thrushes and Blackbirds. In an examination of 43 Fieldfares in Moldavia, three species were found, one on five birds, one on eight and the other on 19, with a maximum of 92 samples on one bird. Another study in Austria, also of 43 Fieldfares, found five species of *Mallophaga*, the commonest two infecting 31 and 29 of the birds. The blood-sucking ticks and fleas are perhaps more likely to weaken their host but have been little studied on Fieldfares. In a four-year examination of 199 Fieldfare nests in Switzerland, no ectoparasites at all were found in two of the years, but two nests contained mites, and flat-flies were found in 15 per cent of nests with late broods in the dry year of 1976.

Two of the forms of comfort behaviour indulged in by Fieldfares may help to destroy ectoparasites. The birds occasionally sunbathe, lying prostrate with wings and tail spread; the increased warmth may stimulate parasites to move and so become easier for the bird to remove, and the exposure to sunlight also helps the synthesis of vitamin D from preen-gland oil. Fieldfares have been seen 'anting', sitting on an anthill with the feathers fluffed out to allow ants to crawl over them; the ants spray the intruding bird with formic acid, their normal defence against attackers, which may help to eradicate parasites in the plumage.

Moult

Despite daily maintenance, birds' feathers undergo substantial wear. Sunlight, even in northern Europe, tends to bleach the pigments and weaken the feathers. Contact with vegetation will abrade the feather tips, and lighter-coloured parts of feathers wear away more quickly than dark ones. Feathers in poor condition will not efficiently perform their functions of insulation and flight. Birds try to keep their plumage in as good a condition as possible, by cleaning and preening every day. Even so, the feathers gradually wear out. All birds cope with this by growing a new set of feathers generally once a year, usually just after the breeding season. Migratory birds have the choice of moulting on or close to their breeding grounds, delaying migration until moult is almost complete, or migrating to their wintering grounds first and then moulting. Some similar species adopt different strategies: British-breeding Blackcaps, for instance, moult in July and August before going south, while their closest relative, the Garden Warbler, migrates to Africa and moults there.

Adult Fieldfares, in common with all of the European thrushes, have their complete post-breeding moult before leaving their breeding area. Of the various major tracts of feathers, the moult of the tertials (the innermost

Fieldfares occasionally sunbathe.

Fieldfares often look very fat in cold weather when they fluff up their plumage to keep warm.

three secondaries) is completed first, the new tail grows in about the same time as the primaries, but the secondaries are the last to complete their moult, not being fully replaced until about thirteen days after the primaries. The total time during which some of these major feathers are growing, and when the birds are unlikely to undertake any long-distance movements, is about 70 days at Kvismaren in central Sweden, with average dates of 27 June to 5 September. In Finland, the average duration of primary moult is about 51–56 days, possibly up to six days quicker than in central Sweden. It is probably true, as it is known to be for Redwings, that the moulting period is shorter at more northern and eastern sites.

Most of the main feathers are moulted in a standard order. Both wings are moulted symmetrically, starting with the innermost primary, near to the middle of the wing, and the moult proceeds descendently, towards the outside of the wing. The first three or four primaries are dropped quickly, often almost simultaneously, then the tertials are lost at about the same time as the fifth primary. The middle tertial (8th secondary) is usually the first to go, followed by the smallest (9th) and then the longest (7th), although about a quarter of birds show a different sequence. When the first five or six new primaries are fully grown, the moult of the secondaries starts, with the outermost, nearest the middle of the wing, and goes ascendantly, towards the body, although the 6th (innermost) secondary feather is often shed before the 5th. The tail moult starts at about the same time as the 3rd or 4th primary, when the two innermost old tail feathers are dropped, and proceeds centrifugally, towards the outside of the tail, with the outermost tail feathers finishing at about the same time as the outermost wing feathers. With fifteen wing feathers (not including the tertials) to be grown in a period of not much over two months, obviously a number of feathers will be in moult at the same time. Swedish Fieldfares have an average of 4.5 growing wing feathers (primaries or secondaries) at a time, while German birds average about 2.3 simultaneously in moult.

The timing of the onset of moult has been recorded for a few Fieldfares (eleven males and fourteen females) in north Germany: three started in late May, another three in early June and twelve in mid-June, with four in late June and the last three in early July (Lübcke and Furrer 1985). It is apparently normal for Fieldfares to begin their full moult before they have finished feeding their young chicks, whereas Blackbirds do not start until fifteen days after they have finished their breeding duties. In this respect, Fieldfares parallel the corvids and other big birds that have a lengthy moult.

For many species there seems to be a link between the beginning of the autumn migration and the end of moult. The Fieldfare has neither a particularly protracted moult nor an early migration, and this raises the intriguing question of what has driven the evolution to such an early moult, apparently adding to the substantial physiological load of the breeding season. The answer probably lies in the Fieldfare's feeding ecology. It is likely that the birds need invertebrate food to grow sufficiently robust feathers. After the end of the summer, fewer insects and worms are available, so that the birds flock together to find suitable feeding places in the post-breeding dispersal, before the migration proper. It may be only on the breeding grounds that there is sufficient high-quality food.

During its moult, a typical Fieldfare will have only about 80 per cent of its normal usable wing area: most birds do not fly much and become rather secretive. Few ornithologists have studied Fieldfares during moult, but it is probably one of the most important periods of a bird's life, since the quality of feathers grown will affect its survival for the whole of the next year.

Part-way through the annual moult, the new, growing feathers contrast with the worn and slightly bleached outer primaries.

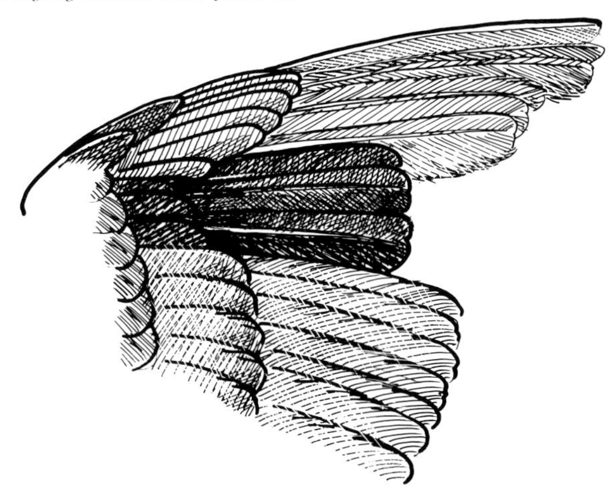

While adult birds undergo a full moult, first-years have a partial moult, growing some new wing-coverts, head and body feathers, but never the primary or secondary wing feathers or the tail feathers. They thus keep the wing and tail feathers that they grew in the nest until after they have bred the next summer, i.e. for about 13 – 14 months. The new feathers usually differ from the 'old' ones in shape, colour and texture, as well as in the degree of wear, and it is these differences that enable ringers to distinguish first-year birds from older individuals.

Most ringers will routinely look at the greater coverts, where there is usually a clear difference in size between the old and the new greater coverts, but there is little recorded information on the extent of Fieldfares' post-juvenile moult. Ruth Lidauer studied the skins of 62 winter visitors to lower Austria and fourteen birds that had died while on migration at Heligoland. She found that the lesser and median coverts were always moulted. There was much individual variation in the moult of the greater coverts, with all of her birds having moulted the innermost two greater coverts, and most having four to five new feathers (mean of 4.7); 22 of the 76 birds had asymmetric moult of the greater coverts, with one or two more feathers moulted on one wing than on the other. Five of the Austrian birds had new carpal coverts. Although these Fieldfares were from two different populations, the Heligoland birds being breeders from Scandinavia and the Austrian wintering birds probably being Polish and Russian breeders, there were no obvious differences in their post-juvenile moult patterns. Twenty seven Fieldfares studied in the autumn at the Swiss ornithological station, Col de Bretolet, showed a lot of variation, having from two to seven new greater coverts with a mean of 5.1. Svensson (1992) states that some juveniles moult all of their greater coverts, but this has not been reported by others.

The moult of the small feathers has been thoroughly studied by Haas. It starts on the underparts with the feathers of the breast and flanks, and then goes on to the belly and undertail-coverts. Simultaneously, on the upperparts, the moult starts from the boundary of the red-brown mantle and the grey rump and progresses towards the head and tail, with the feathers of the nape and neck being the last to go. In the wing, the lesser coverts are moulted first. All of this sequence is the same for adult and first-year birds. In juveniles, the 'eye-stripe' is moulted out very early. Lidauer stated that the post-juvenile moult took place mainly during August-September, being completed before the start of the autumn migration, although early individuals begin in July and late ones continue into October. Most hand-reared Fieldfares started their post-juvenile moult five to six weeks after their wings were fully grown, although one delayed this until after ten weeks.

7

MOVEMENTS

The movements undertaken by Fieldfares are complex and variable. In some populations some of the birds attempt to stay in or near their breeding area throughout the year, such as those that remain to winter in Siberia and in the countries of Fennoscandia south of 65°N. In the world of Fieldfares this way of life is very much the exception, however, and most individuals in most populations are strongly migratory. The extent of the movements varies greatly from one year to another, and from one individual to another, and, in the extreme, a bird may be almost continuously roaming, spending no more than a few weeks, and sometimes perhaps only a few days, in any one place throughout its life.

The breeding and wintering distributions of the Fieldfare were given in Chapter 2, and here the movements between their different haunts are described. Most of the detail about migration has come from records of ringed birds, some of which are used to illustrate this chapter. Some Fieldfares have undertaken prodigious journeys, the longest on record being from eastern Siberia to the west coast of France, over 6100 km.

The Fieldfare's year

As early as June, young birds from early broods form large flocks and leave the adults' breeding territories, thus reducing the feeding pressure on nearby pastures. The young from later broods tend to leave their natal areas with their parents, and move, initially, within a radius of perhaps 10 km of the birthplace.

In early autumn, many Fieldfares from Sweden and Finland move into Norway. This western movement is mainly of first-year birds, and indeed Swedish-ringed nestlings have been found in Norway even as early as July. In August, substantial influxes are found on the Friesian Islands off the Netherlands. These are probably birds that have made the direct flight from Scandinavia.

The best information on the general timing of migration comes from the detailed records kept by the long-established observatories. On Fair Isle, Shetland, autumn migrants occur rarely in August and more regularly from mid-September, although occasionally there are no birds until early October. The main 'falls' on Fair Isle are seldom before mid-October, and the main passage period is normally late October and early November; fairly late arrivals continue to early December in some years.

In Denmark and at Heligoland, the world's first bird observatory, the autumn migration usually begins in the second half of October, lasting to December. On the German coast at Mecklenburg, typically migration is obvious from September to November with the peak in mid-October. At

A first-year Fieldfare on a frosty morning

Berlin, as in northern France, the main passage is from the end of October to mid-November. In the south of France, Provence sees the earliest Fieldfares at the end of September, presumably French- and Swiss-bred birds, with the peak of arrivals in December. In Switzerland, immigrants usually arrive in November or December. In the far south of the wintering areas Fieldfares are usually not observed until January or February, with extreme dates varying considerably from year to year.

Fieldfares, like other thrushes, will migrate by both day and night, although they usually take off at around dusk for the main autumn migration from Scandinavia. Birds gather at sites all along the coast and may wait for several days until the weather seems suitable before setting out. The distance from the Norwegian coast to Scotland is about 600 km, and the typical flight speed of Fieldfares is probably in the range 30–40 km per hour in still air. Thus, the journey will take from 15 to 20 hours of continuous flying, with no chance of a rest. Favourable winds will considerably shorten the flight time, while adverse winds may fatally prolong it.

The usual overnight flight pattern of all the autumn migrating thrushes from Scandinavia is on a broad front across the North Sea. The extensive radar studies carried out in the late 1950s and early 1960s showed that flocks of Fieldfares were typically dense at heights of up to 5000 feet (about 1500 m), with some flocks up to 10,000 ft (about 3000 m). In overnight flights they gradually descend almost to sea level after about midnight. It has been suggested that birds migrating on dark nights might use the direction of waves to orient themselves. If the wind direction is constant and the birds keep flying at a constant angle to the wave fronts, they should be able to maintain their desired bearing, and perhaps this explains the descent to sea level.

As the first scattered rays of sunlight struggle over the horizon, migrating thrushes undertake a rapid 'dawn ascent' while they are well out over the sea, often far from sight of land. Following the dawn ascent, which has not been detected in spring return movements, some birds subsequently reorient in a south-easterly direction, and this may be an adaptation towards eventually making a safe landfall somewhere. Gaining the extra height obviously takes energy, and may be a means of avoiding any predators, such as the big gulls, that try to take advantage of tired migrants, but it will also give them a better chance of seeing land far ahead. Nevertheless, some birds miss landfall in the British Isles, and flocks of Fieldfares have been seen from weather ships 890 km west of Orkney. A recent addition to the topography of the North Sea has been the oil and gas platforms, which frequently burn off plumes of gas. Early suggestions were made that these flares, being visible for several kilometres at night, lured migrating birds to a horrible death by fire, but detailed study has shown that the numbers of birds attracted to the flares is small, and very few are killed. On nights with mist or low cloud, however, autumn migrant thrushes, including hundreds or thousands of Fieldfares, have been seen circling a flare, as they do at lighthouses, and some of them probably become disorientated and die from exhaustion.

Although there are obvious disadvantages to a direct crossing of the North Sea, relatively few Fieldfares make their way to Britain via the continental mainland, and only thirteen Fieldfares ringed in the Netherlands have subsequently been found in Britain, all in eastern and south-eastern England.

On misty nights, migrating Fieldfares may be attracted to a lighthouse or a gas flare.

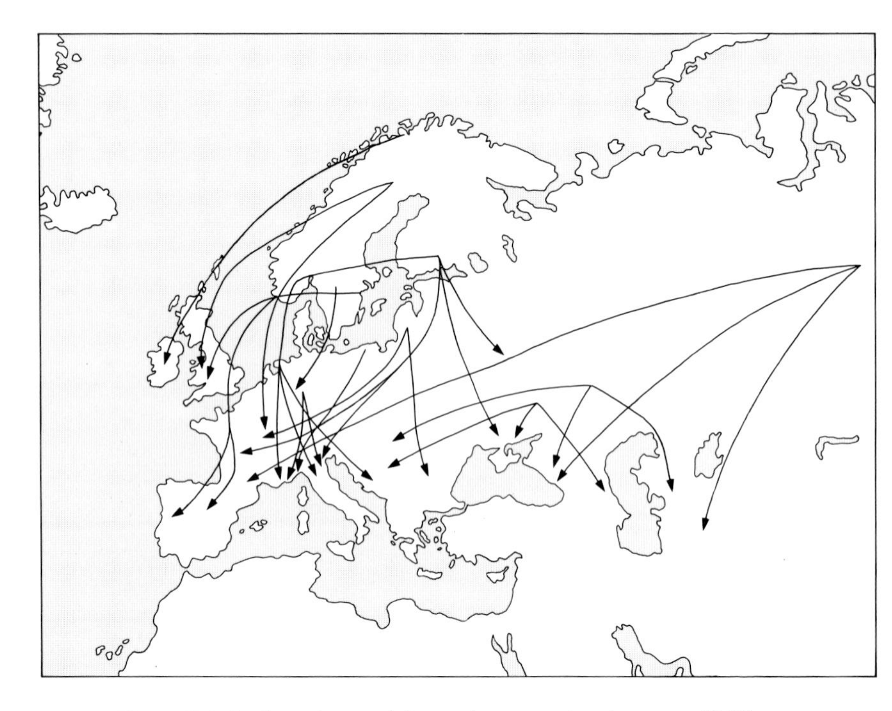

Figure 7.1 *A schematic map of the usual autumn migration routes. Fieldfares may stop almost anywhere along the route, not just at the arrow-head.*

After their initial arrival in Britain, the autumn build-up in midland and western counties is sometimes slow, possibly because birds arriving on the east coast tend to stay until they have exhausted the supply of favourite foods such as the Sea-buckthorn. It is often November before Fieldfares are seen in any numbers. Most British records are of small gatherings of 200 – 300 birds, but up to 600 are often seen together and larger parties of up to 1000 are not unusual. Large concentrations, of up to 15,000, are occasionally found.

During winter, occasional influxes of Fieldfares have been recorded. On Fair Isle, a late wave of movement, apparently unrelated to hard weather and sometimes involving several hundred birds, reaches the island occasionally in the last two weeks of December or in early January. On Heligoland, odd winter flights have been noted up to mid-February. Similarly, on 6 January 1977, 4600 Fieldfares were counted in three-and-a-half hours leaving south-west Sweden. Perhaps these late-moving birds are ones that have stayed late and then exhausted the Rowan crop?

On the other hand, roughly every third or fourth winter Scandinavia is invaded by flocks of Fieldfares, which in some cases remain to breed in the following spring. In the winter of 1936/37 such an invasion occurred, but it came exceptionally late, in January, great movements occurring at Heligoland at the same time. At least 1000 appeared on the Bothnian coast on 26 January, and later they flooded the town of Skellefteå and were estimated at 'several tens of thousands'. From 28 January onwards, thousands of Fieldfares turned up at Stockholm and other places nearby. In the very first days of February large flocks in Umeå were accompanied by Waxwings, both species feeding on Rowan berries, of which there was a fine crop. This late-winter invasion of Scandinavia coincided with the exceptional emigration that led to the colonization of Greenland (see Chapter 2). Large-scale, mid-winter irruptions into Finland, Latvia and Estonia have also been noted, and the most recent influx into Sweden was in winter 1992/93. No ringed bird has ever been found in these mid-winter irrupting flocks, so there is no proof of their origin, but they are unlikely to be from any of the well-studied Fennoscandian populations, and perhaps they come from northern Russia.

In late winter, Fieldfares start to return towards their breeding areas, although, even then, birds that have tried to stay the winter through in Norway may be pushed out by frost or snow. By February, most Fieldfares have left their southernmost wintering areas, especially the south of France and Iberia. The flow of early-returning birds steadily increases during March, but some have already penetrated beyond the Arctic Circle in Norway by early March. Even so, Fieldfares have to be prepared to retreat if conditions worsen, and sudden movements of quite large numbers as a consequence of severe weather are recorded across the entire range, with early nests being abandoned at the onset of a late cold spell.

In Britain in spring, the small parties pack together in large flocks prior to their departure for the northern breeding grounds, becoming increasingly restless and making local movements. The majority of Fieldfares leave Britain by the end of April, but it is not unusual to see late birds during the first fortnight in May. Spring passage is generally more visible than that of autumn, with some impressive continuous movements, often totalling several thousand, passing along lines of hills or valleys in a matter of hours. Those wintering in Britain apparently return direct to Scandinavia across the North Sea, and the Dutch year-round atlas showed no increased numbers there of birds passing through in spring. At Fair Isle, spring passage starts in late February or March and peaks in mid-April, with sizeable 'falls' in early May in some years. The Continental observatories at Heligoland, and at Ottenby in southern Sweden, see spring passage from March to May, with the latest in June. At Berlin, return passage is strong between mid-March and mid-April, the timing of the peak varying by a month from year to year, depending on the weather; the latest Fieldfares are seen from the end of April to the end of May, and even into early June.

The main arrivals in Norway are from mid-April, and in Sweden and Finland from late April. The mean date of first arrival in southern Norway is 8 April, while at Mosjöen (65°50'N) it averages 24 April, and at Pasvik/Kirkenes (at over 69°N in east Finnmark) it is in the range 13–22 May. In the St Petersburg region of west-central Russia, large flocks arrive in mid-March and continue until late April. In Siberia, the Fieldfare is said to be among the earliest migrants to arrive, with large numbers in the Tomsk and Archangel'sk areas by mid-April; others, presumably from the most northerly populations, pass through in the first half of May, when the

Tomsk birds are already breeding. They are first recorded on the Yenesei, south of the Arctic Circle, on 10 May, whilst those in the Pechora regions do not arrive until mid-May.

Fidelity to breeding areas

In view of the great capacity of the Fieldfare to colonize new areas, it is particularly interesting to study if individuals have any tendency to return to breed in the same area from year to year. In fact, investigating site fidelity by the Fieldfare turns out to be a frustrating subject, since most workers have found few birds returning to their study areas. Out of 1857 nestlings ringed in seven years by Lübcke in the Eder valley in Hessen, 33 were found as breeding birds in the following year, eleven within a 1-km radius of their birthplace and a total of 30 within 6 km; three moved farther, two breeding 12 km away and another 15 km distant. The mean distance was about 3 km, and there was no preferred direction for their future settlement, except that some birds seemed to move along the valley. In the expanding Swiss population, Robert Furrer colour-ringed 674 nestlings but managed to find only five subsequently breeding, at distances of 0, 1.3, 2, 4 and 10.3 km from their birthplace. Out of 1152 ringed birds, mostly nestlings, from the increasing stock in the Bodensee (Lake Constance) region, Dr V. Haas found only one subsequently breeding, at 3.4 km from its natal site. In Leningrad, 194 nestlings were ringed in four years in the 10-km^2 Gdanov Park, none of which was later found as a breeding bird among the 60 – 80 pairs there, despite intensive study.

A Norwegian study revealed that, of 65 Fieldfares ringed as nestlings in Norway and recovered in Fennoscandia from 10 May to 30 June, 48 were found within 6 km of the nest site. Three Norwegian chicks were found at great distances in the next breeding season, 180 km SSE, 90 km NW and 430 km SW, suggesting dispersal from their natal area.

These studies were of the return of nestlings to the area where they hatched. One might expect adult birds to show greater faithfulness to an area where they had successfully bred, but few workers have had many ringed adults to study. Lübcke found 41 out of his 1480 ringed adult birds to return in the next year, 30 within 1 km of their previous nest, 40 within 6 km and only one farther away, at 13.4 km.

Unfortunately, none of the studies mentions the sex of the birds, so it is impossible to tell if there is a difference in site fidelity between males and females. However, it is clear that few Fieldfares in any of the populations studied return to breed in exactly the same area from year to year.

Movements of different populations

Fieldfares leave the far north and mountainous areas in the winter, but a few remain in south Fennoscandia and some also winter within the breeding range farther south. Wolfgang Lübcke's study population in

RIGHT *'The Fieldfare effect': many northern species benefit from nesting in Fieldfare colonies, including Merlin, Brambling, Wood Sandpiper, Great Grey Shrike, Icterine Warbler, Golden Oriole, Siskin, Redpoll and Chaffinch.*

Hessen produced five records of birds colour-ringed in the breeding season and seen in mid-winter at the same site. It is interesting to note that the small population that bred in southern Greenland was apparently resident, flocks of at least 30 being encountered in winter, although these were very wary of man, probably because of the reaction of the locals in shooting any that came within range. There is strong indication that most of those that winter in southern Norway and southern Sweden are from the local breeding populations, or possibly from farther north, but not from farther east: very few Fieldfares ringed in the latter regions are recovered in Norway after November. A few Blackbirds also winter in their Scandinavian homes, but all Ring Ouzels and virtually all Song Thrushes, Redwings and Mistle Thrushes leave Scandinavia for the winter, as shown by the comprehensive analysis of the migration of all European thrushes, based on ringing recoveries, carried out by Mrs M.J. Ashmole (1962).

The general tendency is for Fieldfares of the Fennoscandian and middle European populations to move in the sector south-west to south-south-west, while those from the European part of Russia move more west-south-west to south-west. The map (Figure 7.1) indicates the normal direction of movements undertaken. Birds from southern Sweden and Finland move west into Norway and then south, wintering mainly in Belgium, France, Germany, the Czech republic, Switzerland and northern Italy. Fieldfares from northern Sweden and Norway move south-west into Britain, Ireland, central Europe, south-west France, north-west Spain and Portugal, and rarely to north Italy and once to Czechoslovakia. Of the Fennoscandian

Most of our detailed knowledge about Fieldfares' lives has come from studying ringed birds.

populations, it is mainly the Norwegian birds that reach Iberia, and only Norwegian and some Swedish Fieldfares reach Ireland.

Of the southern population recovered from November to February, German, Polish and Swiss birds are found mostly in southern France and northern Italy, although usually avoiding the Mediterranean coast. Those from the Baltic Republics, however, spread over a wider range, bounded by Belgium, south-west France, south Italy, Cyprus and Romania. Many Norwegian birds go to the British Isles and Iberia, while most of those reaching north Italy and central Europe are from Finland, Russia and Germany. The tendency for the populations to keep their relative east to west positions is not, however, absolute and – during winter – there is considerable intermixing, even in the winter ranges of birds from Norway on the one hand and those from the Baltic Republics on the other. For instance, the three ringed birds found in Cyprus had moved in different directions, one from Voronezh, Russia, having travelled 1920 km south-south-west, while the other two had gone in a south-easterly direction from Czechoslovakia (1890 km) and from West Germany (2580 km).

The very large area of Europe over which Fieldfares from a single breeding population may be found reflects their nomadic habits. The species is presumably adapted to exploiting local abundances in berries, which may occur in different places in different years. This is well illustrated by the many ringing records of individual birds in successive winters in countries thousands of kilometres apart, and by individuals moving considerable distances within a winter. Some have exhibited extreme examples of change of winter quarters from one year to another, including one ringed in eastern Germany on 25 February 1979 that was in Greece on 20 February 1981, while another wintering in West Germany was found in winter in Cyprus a year later. Birds ringed in mid-winter in England have moved to central Italy and Dalmatia in subsequent winters, while a January bird from Hungary moved the opposite way to be in Bordeaux, France, a year later. One ringed in Co. Antrim on New Year's Day 1982 was shot in Finland at 61°07'N, 21°57'E on 28 January 84, but there is no way of knowing whether it was attempting to over-winter in Finland or making an early return to its breeding area.

At the other extreme, Digby Milwright found some of his ringed Fieldfares turning up again at the same sites in Cambridgeshire and south-west Norfolk on almost exactly the same date in subsequent years, suggesting recurrent passage. In my study, of flocks in hard weather, I have had just one retrap out of over 1000 individuals handled, a bird first ringed on 10 December 1981 and caught again on 29 December 1985.

The recovery map of Fieldfares ringed in Britain and Ireland (Figure 7.2) shows that they are almost entirely of Fennoscandian breeding stock. Most are from southern and western Norway, central Sweden and the southern half of Finland, but straggling as far north as about 65°N, with odd ones on the west coast of Norway inside the Arctic Circle. My own work in Cheshire has yielded records of Fieldfares found in the breeding season in Sweden at 65°01'N and in Finland at 64°05'N. A few Russian-bred birds reach Britain in winter, most being from Karelia, with the one found near Moscow a notable exception.

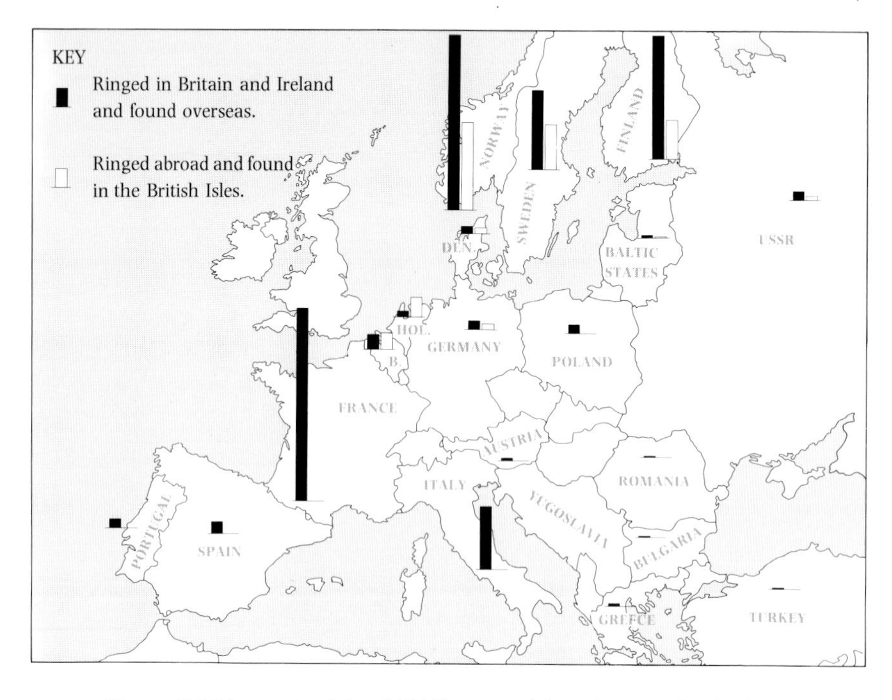

Figure 7.2 *Movements of ringed Fieldfares to and from Britain and Ireland.*

Some British-ringed Fieldfares move west to Ireland or south to France during a harsh winter, such as the one ringed in Hampshire on 7 January 1985 that was found 290 km away in France eight days later. Very severe weather drives some birds farther, as with one ringed in Kent in October 1962 and shot at Gondomar, Portugal, on 10 February 1963, when Britain was experiencing the coldest winter this century. Another was ringed at Gibraltar Point, Lincolnshire on 8 November 1981 and shot 1695 km south-south-west in Portugal on 4 January 1982, after the exceptional frosts and deep snow of 10 – 12 December 1981.

The scattered records in east and south-eastern Europe point to birds taking completely different migration directions in later years, with Fieldfares that have visited Britain in one year being recovered in later winters in Austria, Romania, Yugoslavia, Bulgaria, Greece and Turkey, the last being the record-holder for the longest-distance movement for any British-ringed Fieldfare, 2848 km.

The Dutch atlas of ringing recoveries showed the more easterly distribution of the northern Fieldfares reaching the Netherlands compared with Britain, with almost equal numbers of birds from Finland and the Baltic Republics and from Sweden and Norway. As with Britain, it has not been established to where the Dutch breeders migrate. A bird ringed in the nest in Luxembourg was found in winter five years later near the French Mediterranean coast, 784 km south-south-west. A few Swiss-bred nestlings winter in Switzerland but their main wintering area is south-east France. Ringing returns have shown that French breeders either winter near their breeding sites or move hundreds of kilometres towards the south-west or the south-east.

Within France, Scandinavian Fieldfares winter throughout the country; Baltic birds are found essentially south of a line from the Ardennes to the Gironde; Polish, Czech, German and Swiss birds mostly frequent the south-east, south of a line from the département of Ain, between Lyon and Geneva, to the western end of the Pyrenees. One from the north of France, ringed on 6 March, was found near Moscow on 22 April, seven weeks later and 2350 km away. Fieldfares wintering in Provence have included one from Sverdlovsk (56°37' N, 57°47' E) and nine from Finland, but none from Sweden or Norway.

Some of the most extraordinary journeys undertaken by Fieldfares are those of the Siberian population that have wintered in France in some years. Four nestlings ringed near Krasnoyarsk (56°10'N, 91°25'E) in May 1959 were found in France during January-March 1960, two of them reaching the Atlantic coast of the Gironde, a movement of over 6100 km. It seems amazing that, out of only 906 Fieldfares ringed in the whole of the Soviet Union in 1959, four should have moved from central Siberia to be found in France. Another two from the same area were shot in France in winter 1961/62, while one ringed at Orleans on 27 December 1961 was at Osinniki, near Kemerovo (53°37'N, 87°19'E), on 25 February 1963. Four birds ringed near Prokopievsk (53°54'N, 86°44'E) were shot in France

The darker-plumaged male arrives at the nest with a beakful of earthworms while his mate broods their six small chicks.

between 9 December 1965 and 10 January 1966. Thus, Siberian Fieldfares move far to the west only in certain years, perhaps when the population level is high in the autumn and they fail to find sufficient food in their normal wintering range in the region of the Aral, Black and Caspian Seas. These are the classic conditions for irruption, as found also with species such as Waxwing, Brambling, Jay, Nutcracker, and the crossbill species.

Bernt-Erik Sæther's 1979 analysis of Norwegian-ringed Fieldfares revealed the fascinating finding that adult Fieldfares from Norway migrate farther away from the breeding area than first-year birds, contrary to the norm for almost all other species. For instance, as early as 1939 Sir Landsborough Thomson showed that Gannets in their first and second winters travel as far south as Senegal, whereas older birds are seldom found in Africa. In fact, adult birds in every Fieldfare population migrate farther than first-years, as has been found by Digby Milwright in his special study using results from all the European ringing schemes. The reasons for this are unclear, but certainly the adults are better adapted to long-distance flights by virtue of their longer wings.

Although the general direction of movement in all Fieldfare populations is to the south-west, some individuals move in a northerly direction. For example, a chick ringed in May in its nest near Lake Geneva was found in the Netherlands on 4 October, having moved 590 km north-north-west, and an adult of the west Siberian population, ringed near Orenburg in the south Urals in April, was found in Estonia in October, 2030 km west-north-west.

Finally, whenever bird migration is mentioned, two questions are usually asked: why do they do it, and how do they do it? Whole books have been written on these subjects, of which Thomas Alerstam's *Bird Migration* is a superb example, but brief answers can easily be given for Fieldfares. They move to exploit local abundances of food, with copious earthworms in their breeding areas during the long hours of summer daylight, but mostly inhospitable winters. On the other hand, sufficient berries are available, supplemented by some invertebrate food, to sustain them in the winter quarters. The hazards of making long journeys between their summer and winter haunts are outweighed by the risks of not moving, and natural selection exerts a powerful force to establish favourable traits. If birds that migrate survive to raise more young, then migratory habits will soon become the norm. Birds exhibiting a clearly disadvantageous habit will be wiped out. If there is a balance, with migration favoured in some years and not in others, as seems to be the case with some Fieldfare populations, then both migratory and resident tendencies will coexist within the same species. Like most birds, they navigate mainly by using their internal clock and observing the direction of the sun and stars, with secondary clues from other senses. Although the general facts of migration are now well known, the details of how any individual bird makes its journey are difficult to ascertain by any present-day technique, as the migrants mostly fly over the sea, below radar threshold, and in the dark. Answers to such queries may await the results of futuristic ideas of implanting birds with miniature transmitters and tracking them by satellite.

8

WINTER

To many people in Britain, flocks of Fieldfares are taken as one of the signs of approaching winter. Arnold Boyd, a keen observer of country life, noted that in the autumn the Cheshire farmer hopes to have sown all his winter wheat before they arrive, while in spring, when there are late-lingering flocks, folklore has it that 'we shan't have warmer weather till the bluebacks have gone'.

So long as food is available, Fieldfares can survive the rigours of an Arctic winter. They have been seen on the Norwegian highlands in a temperature of −30°C, and flocks have been recorded in March at Petsamo, some 480 km inside the Arctic Circle, when 1 – 1.5 m of snow lay on the ground. However, such records are unusual, and the timing of the normal autumn departure from Scandinavia depends on the abundance of the Rowan crop, and hence how quickly it becomes depleted. In years with a very heavy crop, large numbers may remain in Scandinavia well into the winter. The autumn and winter Swedish bird census in 1976/77 reported on the timing of movement of Fieldfares. In the north (north of the 60° parallel) the highest counts were in the first period of the census, the first half of October, and numbers decreased dramatically from then onwards. For the rest of Sweden, numbers peaked in November, with substantial flocks still present into the new year but almost all departing between 9 and 29 January, although a few remained in February and March, as far north as Värmland at 59°30'N. Even in normal winters a few Fieldfares usually remain in southern Finland, and when the Rowan has a good berry crop they are even sometimes exceptionally abundant. Such peaks were reported for the winters of 1940/41, 1950/51, 1956/57, 1964/65 and 1969/70. Another abundant Rowan crop led to tens of thousands of Fieldfares staying in Finland in winter 1983/84; most left to the south-west or south in January, but thousands still remained in February. In the winter and spring of 1984/85, there were unusually high concentrations of Waxwings and Fieldfares in Moscow, feeding largely on the abundant Rowan crop, as befits the Russian Drosd-Ryabinnik (mountain-ash thrush).

Heikki Tyrväinen (1970) analysed the mass occurrence in Finland in 1964/65, when Fieldfares were also very abundant in Sweden and odd birds were seen wintering as far north as forest Lapland on the edge of the Arctic Circle. The autumn crop of Cowberry and Crowberry was probably good, encouraging birds to stay late near to their breeding sites. In the southern part of the country, flocks of thousands were seen on some days in December and January. The flocks in southern Finland increased in size from autumn to mid-January, and after that decreased continuously. The Fieldfares left Finland only when the Rowan berries were exhausted,

A flock of Fieldfares in mid-winter, all facing into the wind on the top of frost-covered poplar trees.

weather conditions having but a minor effect. Depletion of the food reserves combined with cold weather led to the formation of some large flocks that moved into towns, where food was still available. The few ringing recoveries overseas were from farther east than usual, according with the observations of visual migration out of Finland after exhaustion of the Rowan berry crop. In that winter, fewer than one-fifth of the normal numbers of Finnish-ringed Fieldfares were reported from foreign countries, suggesting that most of the wintering birds were Finnish-bred. Of course, this does not mean that four-fifths of Finnish birds stayed in Finland, since the numbers of ringed birds reported depends greatly on hunting, which is most prevalent in the autumn around the Mediterranean: if the Fieldfares migrated later than usual, and many of them took a different direction from that in other years, they probably experienced different hunting pressures. Indeed, only one Finnish-ringed bird was reported from France, compared with an average of twenty a winter during the 1960s.

Finnish ringers and winter bird-counters completed questionnaires for 1964/65 and 1969/70. Over both winters, 94 per cent of the respondents reported that the Fieldfares' main winter food was berries of the Rowan, of which there were good or exceptionally good crops throughout the country. Subsidiary food items included the berries of Juniper, Sea-buckthorn and Hawthorn, apples, buds, catkins, and prey collected at dunghills. Rowan berries were available for a long time in 1964/65, at least partly because the Waxwing, which feeds on these berries, invaded southern Finland very late. The snow cover was unusually delayed, making ground food also available. In 1969/70, snow, and the Waxwings, came earlier and the mass occurrence of Fieldfares ended in January, about three weeks earlier than in 1964/65. Again, most of the observers of departing birds reported a flight direction of south or east. Tyrväinen suggested that the birds' migratory instincts are triggered when there are just a few Rowan berries left on each inflorescence.

Despite this variability in Fennoscandian habits, Fieldfares consistently winter in large numbers throughout Britain and Ireland, except in the highlands and the bleakest coastal areas of north-west Scotland. The winter stock in central Europe depends greatly on the extent and depth of snow cover. In milder weather they are found roughly up to the −2.5°C January isotherm, in other words as far east and south as Gdansk, Pomerania, Silesia, Prague and the Vienna basin, where flocks from a few hundred to 2500 birds are widespread. There are sometimes exceptional flocks reported in unusual sites, such as the invasion of over 2000 Fieldfares in the St Moritz/Engadin region of Switzerland in winter 1986/87.

Winter flocks in Cheshire

I have caught and ringed over 1000 Fieldfares feeding in mid-winter in an apple orchard at Daresbury, Cheshire, England, most of them during hard weather in the 1980s. The number of Fieldfares present in the orchard in such conditions was usually 1000–3000, with few, if any, when the ground was unfrozen, and normally there were few birds in this area until frost hit other parts of Britain. I used to set my mist-nets between the rows of apple trees very early in the morning, as the first Fieldfares flew in well before first light. If it had been frosty on the previous day, most birds were caught in the first hour of light. On the first day of frost, there were usually few Fieldfares at first, with numbers building up during the morning, presumably as they realized the difficulty of feeding elsewhere. Some Fieldfares could be caught all day long provided the ground stayed frozen. It was noticeable that many left the orchard as soon as there was likely to be thawing ground somewhere, although often it was not obvious that the temperature had changed: the birds must have responded to more subtle clues than were detectable by man.

Of all Fieldfares caught at the site, almost two-thirds were females, with 16 per cent adult males, 20 per cent first-year males, 22 per cent adult females and 42 per cent first-year females. There was no significant difference between the proportions of each sex caught from one year to another but there was a highly significant difference in the age ratios, with a high proportion of adults (56 per cent) in 1981/82 and relatively few (24 per cent) in 1985/86. This could simply reflect annual variations in the production of young birds. There could also be a different mean distance of movement between years, since birds winter closer to their natal area in their first year than in subsequent winters. Digby Milwright suggested that individual Fieldfares may not stay long, moving on to be replaced by others throughout a winter. Ruth Lidauer and Johannes Dieberger thought that, after about 20 January, the Fieldfare population near Vienna seemed to stay in the same wintering area until the spring migration. It is impossible to tell from my study whether birds of different ages visit the area at different times of year, with one age group, for instance, perhaps moving out of Britain during a winter, because there is no winter with sizeable numbers caught both before and after the year end. This is mainly because of the limited food supply: in years with large flocks present in November and December, there is unlikely to be much fruit left for birds in January or February. The 1981/82 catches were in December, while in most other winters, the hard weather, and the big numbers, came in January.

There are several possible explanations for the high proportion of females, and especially first-year females, in my catches. In winter flocks of Blackbirds in Britain males outnumber females by about 2:1, and a similar ratio is found in the adult Starling population, although there are almost equal numbers of first-year birds of each sex (the differential mortality being caused by the fact that most first-year females attempt to breed whereas most first-year males do not). Lidauer and Dieberger shot 127 Fieldfares for their study near Vienna and found an equal sex ratio, 64 males and 63 females, but counts by Mike Harris (1962) and J.H. Phillips (1961) suggested that there may be a predominance of females in the British wintering population of Fieldfares. Perhaps fewer males reach Britain because they are better at finding food in difficult conditions and more likely to winter closer to their breeding areas (a similar effect is well known for Scandinavian Chaffinches). This could be tested for Fieldfares by examining the mean distance of winter recoveries of Scandinavian-ringed birds, but few recoveries refer to sexed birds as most are ringed as unsexed nestlings and found by members of the public.

I suspect that an important reason for the preponderance of females in the orchard is that apples are a relatively poor-quality food, and birds lowest on the social dominance scale, presumably the first-year females, are the most likely to have to concentrate on them. Maybe the age-dependent variation of black colour on the head is an adaptation to this, with first-year birds looking greyer and thus subordinate to the blacker-looking adults.

As commented on in Chapter 1, the weight of birds is a good indicator of their general condition, and their winter weights reflect how easy or how difficult it is for them to find food. For the 664 Fieldfares that I weighed in hard weather in the orchard, the mean weights are: adult males 114.9 g; first-year males 111.6 g; adult females 108.7 g; and first-year females 108.0 g. Adult males are significantly heavier than first-year males, but there is no age-related difference in the mean weights of females.

The Fieldfares that I weighed were, on average, somewhat heavier than the published figures for those measured in other countries, many of which are summarized in The *Birds of the Western Palearctic*. Bigger, longer-winged, birds tend to weigh more than shorter-winged ones, but only about 10 per cent of the variation in weight is accounted for by variation in wing length for the birds that I measured. The difference in weight that I found between adult and first-year males has not been reported before. Ruth Lidauer and Johannes Dieberger, measuring birds shot during three winters in oak woodland near Vienna, found no significant age-dependence, males averaging 105.7 g and females 102.8 g, somewhat lighter than my birds. Their Fieldfares were living in what is probably a natural winter habitat and the weights are more representative of typical conditions than are those of the Cheshire birds, caught feeding on fruit in hard weather.

Figure 8.1 *Mean weight, with 95 per cent confidence limits, for flocks of Fieldfares caught in Cheshire on different dates.*

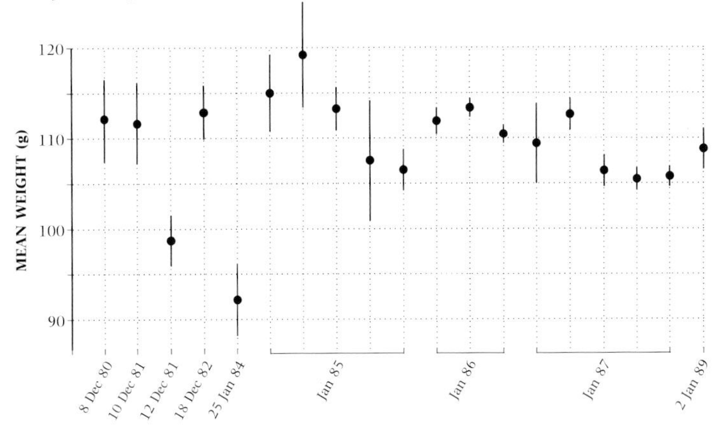

How do Fieldfares manage when the ground stays frozen for some time? In my study, there were prolonged cold spells in three successive winters, in January 1985, 1986 and 1987, where I made several catches over a period of two weeks or more. In each of these months the trend was for mean weights to increase at first, as depicted in Figure 8.1, with the second catch of each sequence showing the highest mean weight, but weights then fell with each subsequent visit. The measurements suggest that, on average, birds put on weight in the first few days of freezing weather, but after that, the mean weights of the ringed birds dropped. This could be because the Fieldfares that are in better condition are leaving the area, possibly flying west or south in the hope of finding unfrozen ground, or that the same population stays around and birds are unable on average to maintain their body weight on a diet of apples alone. In Germany, Wolfgang Lübcke found that Fieldfares died during a long cold spell, despite a sufficient supply of apples, presumably because of a reduced protein intake. As discussed in Chapter 3, Fieldfares probably need some invertebrate food, but apples give them sufficient energy to keep going when the ground is frozen and too hard for them to find live prey. The lightest birds are probably those that cannot find invertebrate food, perhaps because they have failed in competition for areas such as ditch edges that are less likely to be frozen.

There were normally few Fieldfares in the orchard in mild weather. Exceptionally, there were up to 500 birds at the beginning of 1989 when there was no overnight frost and the daytime temperature was above 5°C. There was no difference between the mean weight of birds caught from this flock (shown in Figure 8.1 as '2 Jan 89') and those recorded at the beginning of a cold spell, but there was least variation in the mild weather catches, suggesting that, even at the beginning of cold weather, birds are reacting differently. Hugh Brazier, catching Fieldfares in orchards near Dublin, found the same mean weight of around 112 g for birds caught before and after the year-end, but there was greater variation in the weights in January and February.

Two Fieldfares face up to each other over an apple. The bird on the left is weakly threatening, while the one on the right is strongly threatening.

When the apples have all gone and hard weather strikes, Fieldfares can be really in trouble. One day after the orchards had been stripped bare (25 January 1984), I caught 16 birds from a flock feeding on berries in a Holly hedge, when the Fieldfares managed to overwhelm the territorial defence of two Mistle Thrushes. These birds averaged 91.7 g, much lighter than any group caught in the orchard, as shown in Figure 8.1. The only other day when I found weights averaging less than 100 g was on 12 December 1981, the coldest day in the period of my study, when most birds had moved out after two days of exceptionally severe weather. It is likely that the birds remaining in Cheshire were those not in a good enough condition to fly far.

Several authors have recorded the weights of Fieldfares either killed by frost or in weak condition. J.S. Ash found that eleven frost-killed birds had a mean weight of 56 g. On Anglesey in 1962, Peter Hope Jones recorded four freshly dead with a mean of 58 g, fourteen too weak to fly averaging 63 g, 29 stronger birds with a mean of 78 g, and eleven said to be 'stronger still' averaging 84 g. Wolfgang Lübcke reported the mean of 34 birds found dead in 1978 at Wilhelmshaven to be 63 g, with the first birds found dead after eight days of continuous sub-zero temperatures. Mike Harris weighed 25 Fieldfares killed by hard weather on Skomer in 1962, ranging from 53 to 66 g, with a mean of 58 g; and 33 killed by hard weather in the Netherlands, reported in *The Birds of the Western Palearctic*, also had a mean of 58 g but ranged from 66 g to as low as 47 g.

All these figures support Robert Furrer's statement that a 65 g weight is 'critical'. However, Bob Swann's Fieldfares at Drumnadrochit, Scotland, that fed on sloes and *Cotoneaster* berries lost weight quickly and birds with weights of up to 90 g appeared to be dying; several were found dead within three days of being weighed at 82 – 101 g, with one at 100 g dead within 30 hours. These weights are much higher than those reported from the other studies cited. It is likely that the Scottish birds, at 57.5°N, would have to maintain a higher weight than those in Cheshire and at Anglesey and Wilhelmshaven, all at about 53.5°N, because in mid-winter they have 10 per cent less time for feeding, days being about 45 minutes shorter, with nights correspondingly longer. Although they are larger than

Blackbirds and might be thought, from their northern range, to be more hardy. Fieldfares are apparently less well able to withstand very severe winter weather, possibly because they are less versatile in their feeding ecology. While the Drumnadrochit Fieldfares were losing weight and dying, many Blackbirds put on weight, augmenting their diet of *Cotoneaster* berries with a variety of food put out by man.

In the last catches of the prolonged cold periods in my study, the mean weights of males are about 110 g and of females about 103 g. Even the lightest bird recorded, at 82 g, is well above the critical minimum of around 65 g for hard winter weather and, given continued access to apples, could probably survive a few more days. Apart from in December 1981, however, the flocks at Daresbury dispersed when the supply of apples was becoming exhausted, not necessarily because of the end of a cold spell, and any Fieldfares staying in the area would then face severe feeding difficulties.

Hard-weather movements

In heavy snow or frost, great flocks of Fieldfares are often seen on the move, trying to avoid the worst effects of hard winter weather. This is one of the most impressive and spectacular events involving the species, and the one that brings them to the attention of more people, birdwatchers, country folk and townspeople alike. Perhaps it is no surprise that Norman Elkins's book *Weather and Bird Behaviour* has a jacket illustration by Crispin Fisher of Fieldfares and Redwings moving west in deteriorating weather. Falling temperatures and snowstorms will drive birds from the open countryside and higher-lying land into coastal districts, their appearance there sometimes giving rise to erroneous reports of fresh influxes from abroad. Birds also tend to quit northern Britain in hard weather and move south and west. At such times, Fieldfares may enter gardens and other sites where they are rarely seen. If conditions worsen, increasing hardship may compel further movements until whole counties are deserted.

Such a general retreat was noted, for instance, at Redcar in North Yorkshire on 23 December 1900, when Bannerman noted that 'birds were passing from daylight to dusk, evidently fleeing from the severe snowstorms that broke over Cleveland that night'. The disorienting effect of a snowstorm has been illustrated in a bizarre manner when one bird out of a flock coming in off the sea in snow landed on a man's head and stayed there for a few seconds before rejoining the flock flying inland. Dutch workers report that Fieldfares are usually found on the move in mist, snow or storm, and they often move ahead of a cold front.

In such hard weather, Fieldfares may become unusually plentiful in more sheltered neighbourhoods such as the Hebrides, west Ireland, Cornwall and the Scillies. In recent times, at least 10,000 Fieldfares gathered to feed on apples at Daresbury in Cheshire on 19 January 1986, when blizzards hit most other parts of northern and southern Britain. North Cheshire, being relatively sheltered and benefiting from the microclimate from the inland penetration of the estuarine Mersey, must have been one of the few areas available to them on the British mainland. In the

Two birds confront each other over food but neither bird is prepared to give way, so they match each other's display and end up actually fighting.

more severe winters many perish, while the survivors attempt cross-Channel flights. Even those taking refuge in Ireland may be forced to emigrate, as in 1886 when from 18 to 23 December immense flocks, with other thrushes and Starlings, were seen streaming westwards off Donegal, out into the Atlantic, following their instinct to move westwards, but surely flying to a death through exhaustion.

In bad weather, it is obviously a fine decision how long to stay put in an area known to them, trying to exist on whatever food can be found. The disadvantages of moving out include the energy costs of doing so, the uncertainty of finding conditions any better, and the possibility of increased competition from other birds crowding into the warmer areas. If they delay too long, and the weather does not improve, they may be too weak to undertake a long flight, and then face a bleak outlook.

Some very hard British winters in the eighteenth century are graphically described by Gilbert White, notably those of 1739/40, 1776 and 1784. In 1776 he said that the thrushes and Blackbirds were mostly destroyed, and that in the 'Siberian days' of 1784 the frost killed most of the Ivy and Holly. A great frost from November 1890 to January 1891 lasted continuously for 59 days; the mortality among thrushes was very great, and Fieldfares and Redwings appeared to have moved out of the country altogether.

After particularly hard weather, and a late spring, Fieldfares are often found in their winter quarters well into May, and even June. These birds may be those that are in too poor a condition to move back north and breed successfully. In such circumstances it is suggested that birds of many species may stay in their winter areas: for instance, terns, swifts and Reed Warblers are found in Africa in June, but these are long-lived species and there is a reasonable probability that an individual will survive for another year and have an opportunity to breed then. For a species like the Fieldfare this is a very risky approach, since the average annual mortality is so high that many birds will not live for another year: they have only one chance to breed.

Some Fieldfares, perhaps first-years, possibly ones not in good enough condition to fly far, linger in places as far south as Italy, and cold and wet weather can induce some to stay well south into June. Apart from the few breeding birds, most of the records of Fieldfares in Britain in June and July have followed winters of exceptional severity, and may be presumed to relate to birds that were in too poor a condition to return to Scandinavia. The most obvious examples are where several birds are found together, as with a flock in Cumbria on 11 July 1918, three in an Essex garden on 29 June 1947, and Gilbert White's report from 1740 when, following that 'dreadful winter' of 1739/40, cold north-easterly winds continued to blow on through April and May and Fieldfares (what few of them had survived the winter) did not depart as usual, but were seen lingering about until the beginning of June.

9

SURVIVAL AND MORTALITY

Over 50 years ago, David Lack pointed out the relationship between the number of chicks reared and the survival of full-grown birds. For a stable population, sufficient young have to be produced for the number surviving to the next breeding season to balance the number of full-grown birds dying in that year. For Lack's study species, the Robin, which lays perhaps two clutches of five eggs per pair, on average about nine of those ten chicks will die before the next breeding season, as will one out of two adult birds. This leaves two Robins surviving to found the next generation. So many chicks have to be raised because so many birds die. The implications of the opposite case had been realized even in 1889, when Alfred Russell Wallace in his book *Darwinism* made the simple calculation that if birds produced ten young per pair each year, and all of those young survived to breed with the same statistics, the population would grow 20-million-fold in ten years. Lack's work stunned the ornithological world and at first incurred ridicule, and disbelief that so many birds died, but the figures speak for themselves, and are purely the result of natural selection.

There are two ways of trying to work out the species' survival or mortality rates, neither of them entirely satisfactory. By monitoring a breeding population of individually recognizable adults, marked with colour rings, wing tags or the like, one can see the number of surviving adults and new recruits each year. For this scheme to work well, a closed population is needed, since it is impossible to distinguish any bird that moves to breed elsewhere from one that dies: both are lost to the study area. Most Fieldfares seem to be mobile, with no great tendency to return to the exact area where they were reared or where they bred in the previous year, and the species appears unsuitable for this type of study. In any case, it seems that there are no Fieldfare populations with many marked adults, and this method has not been applied to them.

Survival or mortality rates can alternatively be calculated from the age of ringed birds that are subsequently reported. There are biases inherent in this method as well, particularly when comparing species which are hunted with those that are not, since hunting is an indiscriminate mode of death, and most birds dying naturally are not found by man, whereas most hunted birds are. An analysis of Norwegian Fieldfares, however, found no difference between estimates of mortality from those killed by man and those found dead.

For analysing the annual survival, it is questionable which 'year' to take. It was shown in Chapter 5 that many of the eggs laid do not produce chicks, many of the chicks hatched do not fledge, and many fledglings die in their first month or two of independence. To exclude these effects of high mortality for very inexperienced birds, analyses of mean survival rates often ignore the first two months or so of the birds' lives and calculate from a date such as 1 August. Once a bird has reached adulthood, at one year of age, the mean mortality appears to be constant, or, equivalently, a fixed proportion of adults die each year. There is no sign of an increase in mortality with old age as there is with mankind.

The survival rate for Scandinavian Fieldfares, calculated from ringing recoveries, is lower than for the other members of the thrush family:

	juvenile survival	adult survival
Blackbird	0.43	0.57
Song Thrush	0.47	0.60
Mistle Thrush	0.36	0.52
Redwing	–	0.43
Fieldfare	0.31	0.41

These figures mean that, on average, an adult Fieldfare which is alive on 1 August has a 41 per cent chance of living for another twelve months,

Berries comprise most of a Fieldfare's winter diet.

and a 59 per cent chance of dying within the year. For all of the thrushes, the first-year birds have only about three-quarters the chance of surviving that an adult has. Another study showed the annual mortality for Swiss Fieldfares to be around 60 – 70 per cent, independent of the age of the bird. The high mortality is one of the factors leading to the Fieldfare breeding strategy (see Chapter 5).

These figures for survival rates can be compared with the expectations from the population dynamics. The trend for the five thrush species is unsurprising, with Fieldfares having the highest mortality but laying the largest clutches. With a 60 per cent adult mortality, on average only 0.8 birds will survive a year from each breeding pair. Assuming a roughly stable population, they need to produce a number of offspring that will leave 1.2 of them surviving for the next breeding season. With about 70 per cent annual mortality of first-year birds, this would mean that each pair has to raise on average about 3.9 fledged young. In fact, none of the detailed studies of breeding biology has found such a high productivity, even in the expanding populations, and one has to suspect that the above-quoted figures for survival are underestimates. Typical figures for reproduction seem to average about two fledged young per breeding pair, with up to four per pair produced in some good years. The production of two young per pair would be consistent with age-independent survival rates of 50 per cent, or, if the first-year survival is three-quarters that of adults, with adult survival of 0.57 and first-year survival of 0.43, which are, coincidentally, exactly the figures found for Scandinavian Blackbirds.

The oldest ringed Fieldfare was reported to have been found dead just over eighteen years after its date of ringing in Finland, but no others have been found over ten years old. An 18-year-old bird seems surprising, although a 20-year-old Blackbird and a 19-year-old Redwing are on record. By taking data from 152 species, a general relationship has been found to hold between the age of the oldest known individual and the species' body mass, from which the oldest Fieldfare would be expected to be about eleven-and-a-half years old. The oldest British-ringed Fieldfare was found dead nine-and-a-half years after ringing, with a similarly aged bird from Norway and one at eight-and-a-half years from Germany.

Such old birds are of course very much the extreme, and the average age is much lower. With a mortality rate of 59 per cent (survival rate of 41 per cent), an adult Fieldfare has an average expectation of a further fourteen months of life. If the mortality rate were 43 per cent, the mean expectation would be for an adult bird to survive for a further 22 months.

Death

The most likely causes of death in any population are old age, disease, predation and starvation. The previous section shows that few birds can expect to live to an age where senility sets in. The incidence of disease in wild birds has perhaps been most thoroughly studied for gamebirds and for raptors. Estimates for raptors range from 10 to 25 per cent of deaths attributable to infectious disease or parasitism, and another 10 to 25 per cent to other organic disease, but these are considered by some workers to understate the true figures. Rather few raptors succumb to other predators, but many sick small birds will be killed by predators or starvation before they die of disease.

Recorded instances of disease afflicting wild thrushes are relatively scarce. Most refer to Blackbirds, but Fieldfares are probably susceptible to the same ailments. Bacterial, fungal and viral infections occur and can propagate virulently, including respiratory problems such as tuberculosis, aspergillosis and ornithosis. The virus causing the lethal Newcastle disease (fowl pest) is highly contagious and could spread quickly through a flock. Salmonella, pasteurellosis and other organisms affect the function of internal organs and are likely to prove rapidly fatal.

It is not easy, however, to isolate the cause of death of a wild bird. For instance, those taken by predators are more likely to be ones that have already been weakened by hunger, injury or disease. One winter I ringed almost 800 Redwings at a roost site in Cheshire. Four of these were later found dead by members of the public, all within a few days of each other when two weeks of freezing weather forced the birds to try to find food in suburban gardens; two were taken by cats and one died after flying into a window, but starvation was clearly the underlying cause.

Similarly, a heavy infestation of internal parasites (endoparasites) is likely to weaken or even kill the host, but is unlikely to be obvious enough to be noted by an observer as a cause of death. The main categories of endoparasite are the primitive protozoa and various types of worms, roundworms, tapeworms, thorny-headed worms and flukes. Several species of tapeworm appear to be confined to the thrush family. The nematode roundworms mostly infect the intestines, although some are found in the gullet and others live in the windpipe. Several of the endoparasites have specialized life cycles involving intermediate hosts, such as the fluke *Leuchloridium macrostomum* that relies on small snails to pick up the fluke eggs, which then develop into larvae within the snail; the snails are eaten by birds, especially Mistle and Song Thrushes and Fieldfares, and the flukes lay their eggs in the birds' intestines, from where they pass into vegetation for the eggs to be found by snails again.

One of the few methods that we have of trying to determine the relative importance of some of the manifold hazards facing Fieldfares is to analyse the reported circumstances in which ringed birds have been found by members of the public, but this method also suffers some inherent biases. The proportion of British-ringed Fieldfares found again is about 2 per cent, having declined from 2.2 per cent in the years 1909/60 to 1.8 per cent in the years up to 1980: in earlier times more birds were ringed near to habitation, thus being more likely to be found again. Of 425 recoveries of Fieldfares ringed in Britain, all in winter or on passage, almost one-third were shot or hunted, with another 5 per cent 'deliberately taken by man' and 2 per cent accidentally taken by man; some 3 per cent were killed in traffic accidents, with another 4 per cent colliding with something, 3 per cent were taken by cats and another 2 per cent killed by other predators. The remaining one half were reported merely as 'found dead' or died from other causes.

Rather different figures are found for birds from Norway, which were almost all ringed there in the summer months (Sæther 1979). For Fieldfares in their first two months of life, when they are mostly found locally to their natal area, nearly half were reported just as 'found dead' and are excluded from the following figures: 30 per cent were taken by cats, 9 per cent by other predators, 7 per cent hit wires, while 6 per cent flew into windows or were hit by cars. 48 per cent were deliberately killed by man in various ways. For birds of two months or older, when many birds have moved south-west to areas of high hunting pressure, 86 per cent of those whose mode of death was specified had been deliberately killed by man, 8 per cent were taken by cats and 1 per cent by other predators, while 4 per cent hit overhead wires.

Birds of prey take quite a heavy toll of Fieldfares. In south Scotland, from September to March, Fieldfares made up 8.5 per cent (10 per cent by weight) of 412 items recorded in the diet of the local Sparrowhawks in Ian Newton's study population, this number being exceeded only by those of Redwing and Blackbird. Fieldfares comprised 5.4 per cent of 5698 prey items taken by Sparrowhawks in wooded farmland in the Netherlands. There is no information on the numbers taken by the different sexes. Female Sparrowhawks tend to stay in open country, while males tend to hunt hedgerows and woodland. The larger females, weighing over 300 g, could more easily kill Fieldfares, but male Sparrowhawks, at about 150 g, are certainly capable of killing, and carrying away, Fieldfares weighing on average 120 g. In one French study of Goshawks, the thrush family made up 30 per cent of their winter diet, and doubtless Fieldfares are taken by most raptors if they get the chance.

Peregrines in the Spey Valley in the Scottish Highlands were found by Douglas Weir to feed mainly on passage migrants in spring and autumn, making a particular onslaught on Fieldfares, (plus Song Thrushes and

Fieldfares are frequently taken by Sparrowhawks.

Redwings) from late September to early November. Peregrines wintering on the Essex coast took Fieldfares all through the winter. A British Peregrine nest site has been found 'littered with recently killed Fieldfares', and Derek Ratcliffe's study of prey species near Peregrine eyries in March-July in the English Lake District found that Fieldfare was the most commonly recorded species with 18 per cent of kills. Fieldfares made up around 5 per cent of the corpses found near Peregrine nests in most of the British studies listed in Ratcliffe's classic book on that falcon. Bearing in mind the rather short period of overlap between the Peregrine's breeding season and the Fieldfares' stay in Britain, further work outside the breeding season may reveal that they make up an even higher proportion of this raptor's annual diet.

In a variety of habitats in East Sussex in winter, Fieldfare remains were much more numerous than other species at plucking posts, probably of Sparrowhawks and Tawny Owls, although it is not known whether this was because they were preferred prey, or simply the most numerous species, or the easiest to catch. A Short-eared Owl has been recorded successfully taking a Fieldfare in flight.

Although these studies show that Fieldfares comprise quite a substantial part of the diet of the Sparrowhawk and the Peregrine, it is of course a different matter to determine what proportion of the Fieldfare population falls prey to these predators, and this remains an open question.

Deaths caused by man

In the past, enormous numbers of Fieldfares were trapped for food, with 600,000 taken in one season in the Seventeenth century in East Prussia alone. Stavanger used to be the centre for Norwegian Fieldfare-trapping, and 150,000 were exported in a good year, mostly canned. Even now, Fieldfares come under substantial hunting pressure in some parts of their wintering range, mainly in southern Europe. Within the European Community, the taking of Fieldfares is permitted from September to February in France, Spain, Portugal and Italy, and from September to March in Greece. In addition, there has been frequent hunting in Czechoslovakia and Yugoslavia. They are predominantly hunted with guns. Prior to 1980, 63 per cent of Fieldfares taken had been shot, with 7 per cent trapped and the method of killing the rest not stated. Since 1980, 83 per cent had been shot, with only 2 per cent stated to have been trapped. Shooting of Fieldfares in France has increased significantly relative to trapping.

Research by the British Trust for Ornithology shows that hunting of Fieldfares has decreased substantially in several (though not all) countries and is now a major cause of Fieldfare deaths only in the countries bordering the Mediterranean. Because of the species' mixed and variable migratory strategy, the breeding populations of all countries are at risk, although an exceptionally high proportion (85 per cent) of Fieldfares reported from the Swiss ringing scheme have been killed by man: most of this population has the misfortune to winter in northern Italy or southern France, where the annual slaughter is most intense. This probably explains why the survival rate of Swiss-ringed Fieldfares is apparently independent

Many thousands of Fieldfares are shot in winter in the countries around the Mediterranean.

of age. Most of the other causes of death, such as natural predation and starvation, tend to hit inexperienced birds more severely than adults, whereas hunting is largely indiscriminate.

It is not surprising that some Fieldfare flocks frequent airfields to feed on the grassland. In the UK, five were recorded as being killed by aircraft, in five separate incidents, during 1966–76. The recent practice of allowing grass to grow longer on airfields has greatly reduced the numbers of Fieldfares using this habitat.

10

CONSERVATION

The Fieldfare is an adaptable species that has prospered and spread widely in recent decades. As breeders they have reached countries as far apart as Greenland and Greece, colonizing habitats as disparate as open moorland and city-centre parks. In winter they can survive in Russia and Scandinavia, while others move as far as North Africa or the Canaries.

Fieldfares are attractive to ornithologists, but also to hunters, and have come under substantial pressure from shooters and trappers in many parts of Europe. The hunting of Fieldfares has decreased substantially since 1980, particularly in Norway, Denmark and Belgium, but it has increased in France, where the Fieldfare is still legal quarry, possibly because hunters have turned to thrushes as protection has been extended to other species. It is now a major threat only in countries bordering the Mediterranean, but it is not easy to determine if hunting affects the species' population.

Generally, Fieldfares are not endangered and they probably need few active conservation measures. In an experiment in Norway, substantially increased breeding numbers of Fieldfares were brought about by shooting Hooded Crows locally and destroying their nests, but at the expense of 130 dead crows.

Pasture with abundant earthworms is their preferred feeding habitat in the breeding season. In areas of good habitat but without suitable natural nesting trees, it is possible that Fieldfares could be encouraged to nest by provision of artificial nest platforms. The 'Fieldfare effect', where several northern species breed more successfully within Fieldfare colonies, means that conservation of some other species may be best achieved by establishing and conserving Fieldfares. Merlins and Golden Orioles are among the scarcer birds whose future prospects could be improved in this way. In Britain, the Fieldfare is on the edge of its breeding range, and Leo Batten and his co-authors considered it likely that it may slowly expand. They cited human disturbance as one of the threats to the species' successful colonization, but adherence to national legislation ought to prevent this.

The Fieldfare's favoured feeding areas in winter are predominantly permanent grass fields and hedgerows. Its winter survival may be adversely affected by the restrictions on dairy farming, with a reduction in the area of short-grazed grass, and by the continued destruction of hedges, reducing the crop of natural fruits. Commercial apple orchards provide an important fall-back food in hard weather, and flocks might occasionally cause some economic damage to orchard fruits, although normally their diet contains mainly invertebrates that damage agriculture.

Despite these various possible threats facing them, however, Fieldfares are thriving: long may they continue to do so!

Select Bibliography

In writing this book I have consulted well over 200 published works, including books, papers and theses. This bibliography is a selection of those that are likely be the most interesting for those desiring 'further reading', and are most accessible to British readers.

Alerstam, T., *Bird Migration*, Cambridge University Press, Cambridge, 1990

Andersson, M., and Wiklund, C.G., 'Clumping versus spacing out: experiments on nest predation in Fieldfares (*Turdus pilaris*)', *Anim. Behav.* 26 (1978), 1207–12

Ashmole, M.J., 'The migration of European Thrushes: a comparative study based on ringing recoveries', *Ibis* 104 (1962) 314–46, 522–59

Bannerman, D.A., *The Birds of the British Isles. Vol. III*, Oliver & Boyd, Edinburgh, 1954

Batten, L.A., et al. (eds), *Red Data Birds in Britain*, Poyser, Calton, 1991

Berthold, P., 'The control and significance of animal and vegetable nutrition in omnivorous songbirds', *Ardea* 64 (1976), 140–54

Bochenski, Z., 'Nesting of European members of the genus Turdus', *Acta Zool. Cracov.* 13 (1968), 349–432

Campbell, B., and Lack, E. (eds), *A Dictionary of Birds*, Poyser, Calton, 1985

Cramp, S. (ed), *The Birds of the Western Palearctic, vol. V*, Oxford University Press, Oxford, 1988

Furrer, R.K., 'Seasonal changes in nest site selection of the Fieldfare *Turdus pilaris*', *Ornis Scand.* 11 (1980), 60–4

Glutz von Blotzheim, U.N., and Bauer, K.M., *Handbuch der Vögel Mitteleuropas, Band* 11/II. Aula–Verlag GmbH, Wiesbaden, 1988

Gudmundsson, F., 'The effects of the recent climatic changes on the bird life of Iceland', *Proc. 10th Int. Orn. Congr.* (1951), 501–14

Haas, V., 'Colonial and single breeding in Fieldfares, *Turdus pilaris* L.: a comparison of nesting success in early and late broods', *Behav. Ecol. Sociobiol.* 16 (1985), 119–24

Håland, A., 'Breeding ecology of alpine breeding Fieldfares *Turdus pilaris*', *Ann. Zool. Fenn.* 21 (1984), 405–10

Håland, A., 'Nest spacing and antipredator behaviour of the Fieldfare *Turdus pilaris* in alpine habitats', *Fauna norv. Ser. C. Cinclus* 12 (1989), 11–20

Hickling, R.A.O., *Enjoying Ornithology*, Poyser, Calton, 1983

Hogstad, O., 'Improved breeding success of Fieldfares *Turdus pilaris* nesting close to Merlins *Falco columbarius*', *Fauna norv. Ser. C. Cinclus* 5 (1982), 1–4

Hogstad, O., 'Is nest predation really selecting for colonial breeding among Fieldfares *Turdus pilaris*?', *Ibis* 125 (1983), 366–9

Hogstad, O., 'Nest defence by Fieldfares *Turdus pilaris* towards a human intruder', *Fauna norv. Ser. C. Cinclus* 14 (1991), 83–7

Hogstad, O., 'Nest defence and physical condition in Fieldfares *Turdus pilaris*', *J. Orn.* 134 (1993), 25–33

Hutchinson, Clive D., *Birds in Ireland*, Poyser, Calton, 1989

Lack, P.C. (ed.), *The Atlas of Wintering Birds in Britain and Ireland*, Poyser, Calton, 1986

Lidauer, Ruth M., and Dieberger, Johannes, 'Längenmaße und Gewichte bei Wien überwinternder Wacholderdrosseln *Turdus pilaris*', *Egretta* 26 (1983), 15–23

Lübcke, W., and Furrer, R., *Die Wacholderdrossel* (Die Neue Brehm-Bucherei 569), A. Ziemsen Verlag, Wittenberg Lutherstadt, 1985

Newton, I., *The Sparrowhawk*, Poyser, Calton, 1986

Nicholson, E.M., *Birds and Men*, Collins, London, 1951

Otto, C., 'Environmental factors affecting egg weight within and between colonies of Fieldfare *Turdus pilaris*', *Ornis Scand.* 10 (1979), 111–16

Ratcliffe, D., *The Peregrine Falcon*, Poyser, Calton, 1980

Sæther, B-E., 'Mortality and life history of the Norwegian Fieldfares (*Turdus pilaris*) based on ringing recoveries', *Fauna norv. Ser. C. Cinclus* 2 (1979), 15–22

Salomonsen, F., 'The immigration and breeding of the Fieldfare (*Turdus pilaris* L.) in Greenland', *Proc. 10th Int. Orn. Congr.* (1951), 515–26

Sharrock J.T.R., *The Atlas of Breeding Birds in Britain and Ireland*, BTO, Tring, 1976

Simms, E., *British Thrushes*, Collins, London, 1978

Slagsvold, T., 'The Fieldfare Turdus pilaris as a key species in the forest bird community', *Fauna norv. Ser. C. Cinclus* 2 (1979), 65–9

Slagsvold, T., 'Habitat selection in birds: on the presence of other bird species with special regard to *Turdus pilaris*', *J. Anim. Ecol.* 49 (1980), 523–36

Slagsvold, T., 'Egg predation in woodland in relation to the presence and density of breeding Fieldfares *Turdus pilaris*', *Ornis Scand.* 11 (1980), 92–8

Slagsvold, T., 'Clutch size, nest size and hatching asynchrony in birds: experiments with the Fieldfare (*Turdus pilaris*)', *Ecology* 63 (1982), 1389–99

Slagsvold, T., and Sæther, B-E., 'Time of egg-laying and clutch size variation in the Fieldfare *Turdus pilaris*', *Fauna norv. Ser. C. Cinclus* 2 (1979), 53–9

Snow, D.W., 'Fieldfare', in Lack, P.C. (ed), *The Atlas of Wintering Birds in Britain and Ireland*, Poyser, Calton, 1986

Snow, B., and Snow, D.W., *Birds and Berries*, Poyser, Calton, 1988

Speek, B.J., and Speek, G., *Thieme's Vogeltrekatlas*, Thieme, Zutphen, 1984

Svensson, L., *Identification Guide to European Passerines*, Stockholm, 1992

Swann, R.L., 'Fieldfare and Blackbird weights during the winter of 1978–79 at Drumnadrochit, Inverness-shire', *Ringing & Migration* 3 (1980), 37–40

Thom, Valerie M., *Birds in Scotland*, Poyser, Calton, 1986

Tye, A., 'Economics of experimentally-induced territorial defence in a gregarious bird, the Fieldfare *Turdus pilaris*', *Ornis Scand.* 17 (1986), 151–64

Tyrväinen, H., 'The mass occurrence of the Fieldfare *Turdus pilaris* in the winter of 1964/65 in Finland', *Ann. Zool. Fenn.* 7 (1970), 349–57

Tyrväinen, H., 'The winter irruption of the Fieldfare *Turdus pilaris* and the supply of rowan-berries', *Orn. Fenn.* 52 (1975), 27–31

Wiklund, C.G., 'Increased breeding success for Merlins *Falco columbarius* nesting among colonies of Fieldfares *Turdus pilaris*', *Ibis* 121 (1979), 109–11

Wiklund, C.G., 'Fieldfare (*Turdus pilaris*) breeding success in relation to colony size, nest position and association with Merlins *Falco columbarius*', *Behav. Ecol. Sociobiol.* 11 (1982), 165–72

Wiklund, C.G., 'Fieldfare *Turdus pilaris* breeding strategy: the importance of asynchronous hatching and resources needed for egg formation', *Ornis Scand.* 16 (1985), 213–21

Wiklund, C.G., and Andersson, M., 'Nest predation selects for colonial breeding amongst Fieldfares *Turdus pilaris*', *Ibis* 122 (1980), 363–6

Scientific Names of Species

All species mentioned in the text are listed below, with their scientific names.

BIRDS
Gannet *Morus bassanus*
Bittern *Botaurus stellaris*
Shoveler *Anas clypeata*
Tufted Duck *Aythya fuligula*
Black Kite *Milvus migrans*
Red Kite *M. milvus*
Goshawk *Accipiter gentilis*
Sparrowhawk *A. nisus*
Buzzard *Buteo buteo*
Osprey *Pandion haliaetus*
Kestrel *Falco tinnunculus*
Merlin *F. columbarius*
Hobby *F. subbuteo*
Peregrine *F. peregrinus*
Coot *Fulica atra*
Dotterel *Charadrius morinellus*
Green Sandpiper *Tringa ochropus*
Wood Sandpiper *T. glareola*
Turnstone *Arenaria interpres*
Black-headed Gull *Larus ridibundus*
Lesser Black-backed Gull *L. fuscus*
Herring Gull *L. argentatus*
terns *Sternidae*
Woodpigeon *Columba palumbus*
Cuckoo *Cuculus canorus*
Little Owl *Athene noctua*
Tawny Owl *Strix aluco*
Short-eared Owl *Asio flammeus*
swifts *Apus* spp.
bee-eaters *Merops* spp.
Great Spotted Woodpecker *Dendrocopos major*
Skylark *Alauda arvensis*
Sand Martin *Riparia riparia*
Swallow *Hirundo rustica*
Meadow Pipit *Anthus pratensis*
Waxwing *Bombycilla garrulus*
Wren *Troglodytes troglodytes*
Dunnock *Prunella modularis*
Robin *Erithacus rubecula*
Nightingale *Luscinia megarhynchos*
Rock Thrush *Monticola saxatilis*
Blue Rock Thrush *M. solitarius*
White's Thrush *Zoothera dauma*
Siberian Thrush *Z. sibirica*
Wood Thrush *Hylocichla mustelina*
Hermit Thrush *Catharus guttatus*
Swainson's Thrush *C. ustulatus*
Gray-cheeked Thrush *C. minimus*
Veery *C. fuscescens*
Tickell's Thrush *Turdus unicolor*
Ring Ouzel *T. torquatus*
Blackbird *T. merula*
Eye-browed Thrush *T. obscurus*
Dusky Thrush *T. naumanni*
Black-throated Thrush *T. ruficollis*
Fieldfare *T. pilaris*
Song Thrush *T. philomelos*
Redwing *T. iliacus*
Mistle Thrush *T. viscivorus*
American Robin *T. migratorius*
Reed Warbler *Acrocephalus scirpaceus*
Icterine Warbler *Hippolais icterina*
Garden Warbler *Sylvia borin*
Blackcap S. *atricapilla*
Chiffchaff *Phylloscopus collybita*
Willow Warbler *P. trochilus*
Spotted Flycatcher *Muscicapa striata*
Long-tailed Tit *Aegithalos caudatus*
Willow Tit *Parus montanus*
Coal Tit *P. ater*
Golden Oriole *Oriolus oriolus*
Red-backed Shrike *Lanius collurio*
Lesser Grey Shrike *L. minor*
Great Grey Shrike *L. excubitor*
Woodchat Shrike *L. senator*
Jay *Garrulus glandarius*
Siberian Jay *Perisoreus infaustus*
Magpie *Pica pica*
Nutcracker *Nucifraga caryocatactes*
Carrion Crow *Corvus corone*
Hooded Crow *C. corone cornix*

Raven *C. corax*
Starling *Sturnus vulgaris*
House Sparrow *Passer domesticus*
Chaffinch *Fringilla coelebs*
Brambling *F. montifringilla*
Greenfinch *Carduelis chloris*
Goldfinch *C. carduelis*
Siskin *C. spinus*
Linnet *C. cannabina*
Redpoll *C. flammea*
crossbills *Loxia* spp.
Bullfinch *Pyrrhula pyrrhula*
Lapland Bunting *Calcarius lapponicus*
Yellowhammer *Emberiza citrinella*
Reed Bunting *E. schoeniclus*

MAMMALS
squirrels *Sciurus* spp.
Red Fox *Vulpes vulpes*
Stoat *Mustela erminea*
(American) Mink *M. vison*
Pine Marten *Martes martes*

INVERTEBRATES
craneflies *Tipulidae*
sawflies *Tenthredinae*
stoneflies *Plecoptera*

TREES AND PLANTS
Acacia, False *Robinia pseudoacacia*
alder *Alnus* spp.
apple *Malus* spp.
Ash *Fraxinus excelsior*
Aspen *Populus tremula*
Barberry *Berberis vulgaris*
Bilberry *Vaccinium myrtillus*
birch *Betula* spp.
Birch, Dwarf *B. nana*
Blackthorn *Prunus spinosa*
Bramble *Rubus fruticosus*
Bryony, Black *Tamus communis*
Buckthorn *Rhamnus catharticus*
cherry *Prunus* spp.
Cherry, Bird *Prunus padus*
Chestnut, Horse *Aesculus hippocastanum*
Cloudberry *Rubus chamaemorus*
Cowberry *Vaccinium vitis-idaea*
Crab-apple *Malus sylvestris*
Cranberry *Vaccinium oxycoccus*
Crowberry *Empetrum nigrum*
currant *Ribes* spp.
Dewberry *Rubus caesius*
Elder *Sambucus nigra*
Fir, Silver *Abies alba*
Gean (Wild Cherry) *Prunus avium*
Gooseberry *Ribes uva-crispa*
Guelder-rose *Viburnum opulus*
Hawthorn *Crataegus monogyna*
Holly *Ilex aquifolium*
Honeysuckle *Lonicera periclymenum*
Hornbeam *Carpinus betulus*
Ivy *Hedera helix*
Juniper *Juniperus communis*
larch *Larix* spp.
Lime, Small-leaved *Tilia cordata*
Mezereon *Daphne mezereum*
Mistletoe *Viscum album*
oak *Quercus* spp.
Oleaster *Elaeagnus angustifolia*
Olive *Olea europaea*
Pear *Pyrus communis*
pine *Pinus* spp.
pink *Dianthus* spp.
plum *Prunus* spp.
Poplar, Black *Populus nigra*
Poplar, White *P. alba*
privet *Ligustrum* spp.
Raspberry *Rubus idaeus*
Rose, Dog *Rosa canina*
Rowan *Sorbus aucuparia*
Sea-buckthorn *Hippophae rhamniodes*
Snowberry *Symphoricarpos rivularis*
Spindle Tree *Euonymus europaeus*
spruce *Picea spp.*
strawberry *Fragaria spp.*
Strawberry Tree *Arbutus andrachne*
Sycamore *Acer pseudoplatanus*
vine *Vitis* spp.
Virginia creeper *Parthenocissus* spp.
whitebeam *Sorbus* spp.
willow *Salix* spp.
Yew *Taxus baccata*

Index

INDEX